Sylvan Lake Watershed Stewardship Society

P. O. Box 9012 Sylvan Lake, Alberta T4S 1S6

June 2005

Dear Sylvan Lake Resident,

The Sylvan Lake Watershed Stewardship Society (SLWSS) has arranged for all residents living on or near Sylvan Lake to receive a copy of the Alberta edition of *On the Living Edge: Your Guide to Waterfront Living.* Aptly, we have referred to this SLWSS project as the *Sylvan Lake Shoreline Awareness Program.*

The health of your shoreline is very important to the health of Sylvan Lake. Help protect, maintain and improve Sylvan Lake's shoreline health and, over the long run, enhance the lake's water quality and help protect your investment in your property.

Taking care of the lake benefits us all, and we all can share in it. Start with your shoreline and your riparian area. Encourage your neighbours. Work together. Make your shoreline health an on-going community project. To this end we hope you will find the 148 page tip-oriented book very helpful and will increase your ability to care for the lake and to better enjoy living 'on the living edge'.

We are very appreciative of the Alberta Real Estate Foundation for funding assistance and for the cooperation and support of the Alberta Living by Water Project and the authors, Sarah Kipp and Clive Callaway. Also, our special thanks to the volunteer-members who delivered the books door-to-door and their coordinator Sheila Bosch.

If you would like to join SLWSS, applications are included in the delivery package. Also, we have compiled some web sites that may be of interest to you. See reverse.

Yours very truly,

Kent Lyle
President, Sylvan Lake Watershed Stewardship Society

.

As authors of *On the Living Edge: Your Guide to Waterfront Living,* and founders of *The Living by Water Project,* we are happy to see that Sylvan Lake Watershed Stewardship Society is distributing our book.

We wrote the book when we (waterfront residents ourselves) realized that we were making mistakes that could potentially damage the beauty and quality of the lake that had attracted us in the first place – and could affect our lakeside investment.

We hope that you will find the book useful...and that it will help you avoid some of the mistakes that we made. We encourage you to follow up with the Living by Water Project's Alberta Coordinator if you wish further information (see letter in delivery package).

Sincerely,

Sarah Kipp and Clive Callaway

Caring about Sylvan Lake

Canadian Cataloguing in Publication Data

Kipp, Sarah L
 On the living edge: your guide for waterfront living / Sarah Kipp & Clive Callaway—AB ed.

 Includes bibliographical references and index.
 ISBN 0-9696134-3-1

 1. Shore protection–Alberta. I. Callaway, Clive, 1943- II.
Federation of Alberta Naturalists III. Title.
QH545.S498K563 2002b   333.91'716'097123   C2002-910779-2

Cover photo credits Clive Callaway, Lorne Fitch, Branimir Gjetvaj – www.branimirphoto.ca, and David Park.
Original BC book and graphics design by Dyann Johnson, Dyann Johnson Design Ltd.
Illustrations by Shayne Friesen, Friesen Creative.
Cover design and AB modifications by Carol Dragich, Dragich Design.
Printed in Canada on partially recycled paper by Friesens Printing.

Available in six regional editions across Canada.
To order additional copies of this publication or to obtain written permission from the publisher contact:
The Living by Water Project
c/o The Federation of Alberta Naturalists
11759 Groat Road
Edmonton, Alberta, T5M 3K6
email: fan@fanweb.ca
phone: (780) 427-8124
Website: www.fanweb.ca or www.livingbywater.ca

 This not-for-profit publication was produced with the support of:

WILDLIFE HABITAT
CANADA
HABITAT FAUNIQUE

HOME TO CANADIANS
Canada

Printing supported by grants from the Edmonton Community Lottery Board and the Edmonton Community Foundation.

Disclaimer
The information, tips and ideas in this book have been simplified for readability and ease of understanding. The *Living by Water Project*, its partners, agents, staff, contractors, authors and associate authors, reviewers or sponsors cannot accept any responsibility for any work carried out as a result of the actions recommended in this book. Readers are advised to obtain the necessary professional advice for any work relating to topics discussed in this book including shoreline erosion, bank stability, retaining walls, docks, construction plans and approvals, septic permits, tree condition and removal, or any other actions described.

It is the responsibility of the shoreline resident, or his /her authorized agent or contractor, to obtain all necessary permits, licences, letters of authority and approvals for any work which falls under the jurisdiction of Federal or Provincial acts or regulations, and any Municipal or First Nations or Metis Settlement land use bylaws, development, or building regulations, and to observe and comply with all requirements and standards of any health, environmental, or other lawful authorities.

We recommend that any alterations or corrective measures carried out by the reader be done with due care and attention to human safety and to the structural integrity of buildings and landscape. In many areas (such as erosion control, on-site sewage treatment systems, water treatment and docks), the contents of this book serve as an introduction to the topic. Readers are advised to undertake further research prior to making major expenditures, and to discuss with manufacturers, contractors or other professionals the various alternatives available.

The contents of this publication do not necessarily reflect the views and policies of our sponsors, or organizations who are partners of the Living by Water Project.

*Working towards healthier human and wildlife
habitat along the shorelines of Canada*

Acknowledgements

Many people have assisted in the development and preparation of this book. The support and patience of the sponsors listed on the inside back cover are gratefully acknowledged.

Special thanks go to Glen Semenchuk, Executive Director, Federation of Alberta Naturalists for his faith and patience; to the Federation itself for acting as our publisher; to Cliff Craig of the Rideau Valley Conservation Authority in Ontario for his encouragement; to Anne Murray of the Federation of British Columbia Naturalists who helped with the initial British Columbia version of this book; to the Alberta Conservation Association for funding the poster and to Margot Hervieux and the rest of the Alberta team – Kim Dacyk, Carol Dragich and Claire Classen – who carried out the adaptation.

A number of Living by Water Project staff have worked on this book over several years. Jaci Metivier deserves special recognition for her research and her excellent editing and writing skills in the final production phases of the project. Natalie Affolter provided insightful editorial comments throughout. Shelley Sawada, Simone Palmer, Caroline Sparling, and Erik Sparling helped with some of the early research and writing. A special thanks to Laurisa Gallant for keeping us all grounded.

Our initial inspiration for this book came from the Wisconsin book *Life on the Edge....Owning Waterfront Property*. Co-author Robert Korth has been very helpful and more than cooperative.

Many waterfront residents in Alberta, as well as other parts of Canada, have welcomed us onto their properties over the years and offered comments, questions and ideas. We express our sincere thanks for their help.

We have drawn upon the advice and input of many individuals and organizations in preparing this book. Acknowledgement and thanks for their comments and input at various stages are due to Mike Adams, Keith Anderson, Jeff Beddoes, Warren Bell, Gary Birch, Barry Boettger, Eric Bonham, Cathy Booler, Bob Brodie, Jim Bryan, Dr. Jim Burns, Jim Cooperman, Roy Cranston, Michael Crowe, Katherine Enns, Susan Fisher, Lorne Fitch, John Gallaghar, Stephen Gates, Branimir Gjetvaj, Brian Gregory, Eric Haber, Gerry Haekel, Murray Hamilton, Rick Howie, Mel Kotyk, Stu Lawrence, Colin Levings, Don Meeks, Rick Nordin, David Park, David Polster, Suzanne Rautio, Kevin Rieberger, Mike Richards, John Rowse, Lisa Scott, Jennifer Shamess, Margaret Skeel, Brian Symonds, Trish Wallensteen, Mike Wei, Trevor Wicks and others too numerous to mention, who knowingly or unknowingly gave us ideas, tips and stories upon which this book is built. Sarah's mother, Brenda Weaver, kept us going when times were tough and deserves a special tribute for her interest and support. The original BC book was funded by Fisheries and Oceans Canada, the Vancouver Foundation, Fisheries Renewal B.C., Wildlife Habitat Canada, Habitat Conservation Trust Fund, and Canada Mortgage and Housing Corporation.

We thank Michael Love and *Cottage Magazine* for helping promote this book in the interest of their many readers.

And finally, a very special thanks to our talented and committed designer and graphics consultant, Dyann Johnson. Together with illustrator Shayne Friesen, Dyann has brought this book alive.

In order to keep the price of the book as low as possible we have waived all future royalties. The content has been synthesized from a wide variety of published sources. Primary references are listed on Page 142. While we, and the Alberta adaptation team, acknowledge with thanks the input of others, all errors and omissions remain ours.

Illustration credits

Some illustrations are based directly or indirectly upon previously published works. These are acknowledged below. Full citations are provided in References unless noted otherwise.

Pg 13 A Guide for Buying and Managing Shoreland. Minnesota DNR. 1998. Pg 8 , 9.

Pg 23 Home*A*Syst, An Environmental Risk-Assessment Guide for the Home, Pg 20.

Pg 43 A Primer on Fresh Water. Environment Canada Freshwater Series. 1994. Pg 2.

Pg 51 and 112 Life on the Edge, Pg 15, 41

Pg 55, 58, 59 (top) Lakescaping for Wildlife Pg 43, 32, 46

Pg 59 (bottom) Vegetation Management: A Guide for Puget Sound Bluff Property Owners. 1993. 93–31. Washington State Department of Ecology. Pg 25, 26.

Pg 68 (top) The Role of Vegetation in Shoreland Management, Great Lakes Basin Commission, Pg 13.

Pg 69 Limiting Impact of Recreation on Water Quality. Minnesota Shoreland Best Management Practices No. 5. 1998.

Pg 71 Aitkin County Shoreland Steward – A User's Guide to Shoreland Property 1999. Aitkin County Local Water Planning Task Force, Minnesota. Pg 20

Pg 78 Protecting Fish Habitat, Landowner Resource Centre Extension Series No.44. Manotick, Ont. Pg 3.

Pg 80 (both) and 81 (bottom) Dock Primer, Pg 13, 14, 18

Pg 81 (top) Marine Guide to Small Boat Moorage, DFO Pacific Region. www.heb.pac.dfo-mpo.gc.ca

Pg 97 Bats in British Columbia, Ministry of Environment Lands and Parks. (Brochure.)

Pg 98 Naturescape BC Provincial Guide, Pg 48

Appendix 5 (How Healthy is My Shoreline?)

This checklist is based on ideas in a number of publications, including:

Questionnaire on p. 33 of Caring for the Green Zone – Riparian Areas and Grazing Management. 1995. Cows and Fish Program. Lethbridge, Alberta.

Riparian and Wetland Research Program, University of Montana, Lentic and Lotic Health Assessment (Stand-Alone) Codes and Instructions, 1999

For all life along Canada's shorelines ... and for Becky, Mikael, Ian and Vikki.

Preface

Living near water has its joys, and its occasional challenges. Finding information about how to deal with these challenges can sometimes be difficult, as we've found out over the years we've been shoreline residents. This book is designed to help you find answers to commonly asked questions. For those of you about to build, or who are buying shoreline property, it may even help you avoid some of the mistakes we and many others have made. We learned the hard way. We found that – although we would never knowingly have harmed our property or done anything to potentially reduce its value – on occasion, this was precisely what we were doing!

Until moving to BC in the late 1980s, we both lived in Alberta (Sarah is Alberta-born) and spent many days enjoying its waterways – and big skies! – in the mountains, foothills, parkland and prairie. In BC, we ran a waterfront resort and campground. Besides serving the needs of our customers who had come to relax and enjoy a quiet time by the water, we renovated and built a number of buildings, and managed a major redevelopment project involving roads, water and sewage systems. As consultants, we advised a variety of clients on approaches to waterfront development. And, as members of the community we occasionally volunteered to help with things like cleaning up the local park.

During these busy years we have found that one of the things that has kept us going is living by the water's edge. We think of our shoreline as a very special place; family and friends are drawn to it as well.

It was from our search for simple, tip-oriented information that this book was born. We have drawn extensively on the experiences of other waterfront residents, the stories we've been told, and the questions we've been asked. We have also utilized both published and unpublished materials from many sources, and interviewed officials with government and non-government agencies. This book, originally written for British Columbia, has been adapted for Alberta with the able assistance of Margot Hervieux, Kim Dacyk and Carol Dragich.

On the Living Edge covers a wide range of topics. Our aim has been to provide enough information to get you started, and to provide references for further research.

Over the past years, we have spoken on the phone, and in person, with many of you who live by water, and listened to your stories. We have been inspired by the strong feelings of caring we have heard expressed; as shoreline residents, there is a collective urge among us to protect and look after our lakes, rivers and streams. We hope that this book will provide you with information to assist you in your goals – and save you time, money and frustration!

Sarah Kipp and Clive Callaway
Gardom Lake, British Columbia

Foreword

"On the Living Edge" comes on stream at just the right time. With a friendly, personal style and a few warnings to all of us to take good care of our shorelines, this book contains a wealth of time- and money-saving tips, drawn from the authors' own experiences as waterfront residents and from the experience of others who live by water. You will become informed and wiser by reading this book cover to cover. In a time when shoreline properties – whether in our towns or cities, rural or cottage areas – are getting harder and harder to come by, and when we're also discovering that changes to natural shorelines can have expensive consequences for owners, you'll want to keep "On The Living Edge" as a ready reference for better living by water. Whether you're an owner, a prospective owner, or simply someone who cares about our shorelines, it's in your interest to "do it right" – to look after valuable investments, and safeguard our waters for recreation, fish and other wildlife, and in the case of freshwater, to protect our drinking water. Cottage Magazine has supported the work of authors Sarah Kipp and Clive Callaway in the past and we applaud them in this and all of their endeavours to keep you informed.

Michael Love
Editor, Cottage Magazine

Contents

Living edges, where land and water meet, are the richest, most productive areas on earth. Keeping your 'living edge' natural will give you time to enjoy its uniqueness.

Saving Time and Money ...Naturally

① Introduction

If Only We Had Known!

*T*he day the septic system backed up at the end of our "Welcome to Our Paradise" party, was the day we realized that we needed help. And not just with cleaning the bathroom floor. There we were, city folks who had invested our life savings and followed a dream by moving to the water's edge. But we didn't realize that, when it came to knowing how to manage our shoreline, we were innocent newcomers....

We had figured the septic system would look after itself, and planned to use a left-over bag of fertilizer on the extensive grass area. We pondered extending the dock, paving our driveway, and building a gazebo down by the water, but were too cash-short to do any of those things.

It was a good thing for our lake that our money ran out. For we discovered that even though we loved our waterfront paradise, we were in danger of loving it to death. The very things that had brought us to this tranquil place – its beauty, healthy water, and choruses of birds and frogs – could be affected. We could even see our investment in the property eaten away, as a result of lowered water quality – and property values!

From Streams to Lakes to...

Each year, the numbers of us who own, lease or rent shoreline property increase. Many of you, like us, follow dreams; and perhaps, like us, also jump in without being fully aware of what you might be getting into! In writing this book, we hope to help you – someone who is about to purchase or build, or who already lives on a shoreline property.

On the Living Edge has been written for both permanent shoreline residents and seasonal cottagers along all types of shorelines, both urban and rural. This includes property bordering on a lake, reservoir, or river as well as land containing a stream, pond, wetland, or irrigation ditch. Even if you have a small stream that dries up during the summer, or a ravine that barely has any visible water, consider reading this book.

Shoreline challenges

When we moved to our waterfront paradise from the city, on a snowy winter day, we marvelled at our fortune; living on such a beautiful piece of the earth was something we had only dreamed about.

Late in 1987 we had fallen in love with a rural lakefront property in the British Columbia interior, and impulsively negotiated its purchase. Within two months we had moved from our city lifestyle in Calgary. We soon learned that living beside water is different from living on a regular city lot. We had to cope almost immediately with spring runoff and high water, and the various critters which wanted to move into our home. The lessons we have learned in dealing with these and many other challenges form the basis of this book.

Shoreline property is different. By being prepared for the challenges of waterfront living, you'll be able to spend more time enjoying the benefits. And, with knowledge about "Do's" and "Don'ts", you'll be able to prevent problems from happening and make better informed decisions.

We hope the tips in this book will help you save time and money, avoid frustration, protect the health of your family and visitors, and protect the health and beauty of your property. They may also help you protect the value of your investment, and what will be passed on to your children and grandchildren.

An investment of a lifetime....

Waterfront property is a big investment. In total, about 13% of Canadians, or about 3.9 million of us, have property with water frontage or water running through it. In some areas of Canada, there are also quite a few of us who are from outside Canada – the United States, Europe, Asia. We estimate that there are over 1.72 million shoreline properties in Canada – that's a lot of shoreline!

In 2001, a cross-Canada survey of recreational property (which is frequently waterfront) showed that there are often many more people looking for such property than there are properties available. This means that selection may be limited, competition for properties fierce – and prices pushed upwards. If you're in the market for shoreline property, you may need to make decisions quickly, and you'll want to be well informed about what to look for. Chapter 2 starts you off on this process.

If you've just purchased, you'll most likely be wanting to look after your investment. Perhaps you have dreams about what you will do with your property, and how it will enrich your life. The more you know about shorelines, the more this will be possible.

Because shorelines are different, they need our extra care and attention. It is risky doing things the same way on our shoreline property that we might do on one that is far from water. The day our septic system backed up, we learned that lesson. Septic problems anywhere are annoying, but near surface water, they could cause a serious emergency – and potentially contaminate the water for neighbours.

Did you know ...
A 1996 American study showed that property prices were significantly affected by water clarity in lakes – the clearer the lake, the higher the property value.

A 1998 study in Hamilton, Ontario showed that when the harbour was cleaned up, property values – particularly those close to the water – increased.

Did you know ...
Owners of shoreline property tend to be an older, wealthier group than the Canadian average. In 2001, almost half of us were over 50.

tip **This book is being revised and adapted for other regions of Canada. Check the Living by Water Project website for the status of regional adaptations for other areas.**

The Uniqueness of Shorelines

We built a trail along the shore, and made it wide enough for wheelchairs by pulling trees and shrubs out right to the water's edge. Only six weeks later, it started to erode. We hadn't realized what we were doing....

Lake community representative

Look for the Restore Your Shore icon in various places in this book. This indicates shoreline restoration tips and ideas.

Why shorelines are different

Physical

Shoreline lands often slope, and need special attention when building steps, stairs, paths and roads. Shorelines are on the receiving end of drainage and seepage from uphill. They often have wetter soils which are more easily compacted and damaged than upland soils. Shoreline banks and bluffs can be dynamic and subject to natural changes. They have a tendency to erode because of both slope and the action of water, wind and ice over exposed stretches of water. Surface water is quickly and directly affected by pollution from sources such as poorly placed and maintained septic systems, fertilizer (nitrates, phosphates), driveway runoff, and lawn and garden pesticides. Shoreline properties can be susceptible to the effects of storms and flooding.

Climate

Shoreline properties can be affected by changing lake levels. Shorelines often experience microclimates such as temperature inversions or unusual frost patterns.

Wildlife

Lots of wildlife use shorelines; for example, over 80% of all birds, reptiles and amphibians and 20% of all mammals in Alberta utilize shoreline areas sometime during their life. Shorelines support many kinds of wildlife, including species at risk. Two-thirds of Alberta's "at risk" birds use shoreline areas for all or part of their habitat needs as do four "at risk" amphibians. An additional 22 birds and four reptiles that are considered "sensitive" use shoreline habitats. Shorelines also protect the quality of aquatic habitat for fish and other species.

Legal

Shorelines are governed by a wide variety of laws – federal (such as the Fisheries Act), provincial (such as the Water Act and the Public Lands Act), historic common (such as riparian rights law), and municipal (such as local zoning by-laws designating setbacks and sensitive areas).

Shorelines are "legally dynamic" – that is, the high water line represents a "floating" or variable boundary, defined not by survey pins but by historic high water levels.

The requirement of the law that citizens exercise "due diligence" in the management of their property can have large repercussions for shoreline property. There is increasing civil litigation over problems such as erosion caused by a neighbour's retaining wall, water contamination due to a neighbour's failed septic system, or flood damage caused by runoff.

A healthy shoreline

While shorelines are different and fragile, we haven't always treated them with care. Because it feels good to be near the water, we have tended to build close to it, relying upon our human ability to use technology to surmount nature's awesome power to erode and flood. Fond memories of holidays in warm places can make us try to convert our piece of Canada into a tropical beach paradise. And with our many visitors who, like us, are also drawn to the water's edge, we tend to add more bedrooms to our house, or to build a guest cottage.

As we carried out the research for this book, more and more we came across the term "healthy shorelines". A natural undisturbed shoreline tends to be healthy; this means that it is performing all the many functions that scientists have found shorelines do. In Chapter 3, we outline some of these functions, how they are valuable to you, and introduce some key actions that you can take to have a healthy shoreline.

The bulk of the book is taken up with the two sections *Working With Your Land*, and *Day-to-Day Living*. These contain detailed tips, pointers, and diagrams. The last section of the book is focussed on resources; while some key publications are listed at the ends of chapters, the majority of resources – agencies, websites, phone numbers – are listed in Section 4.

② Thinking of Buying?

Expectations and Reality

We discovered the property on which we now live one evening in early October while searching for a place where we could turn our dreams into reality. A weatherbeaten "For Sale" sign caught our eyes, alongside a sign announcing that the property was a resort. We followed the path down to the water where we saw the sun setting in a dusky pink sky; to the south-east, a full moon was rising, casting its light over the tranquil water. It was love at first sight. We knew that this was where we should be.... From that point on, it would have been hard for anyone to convince us to reexamine our decision. We had made it from the heart.

Probably, as we did, you also have dreams. Perhaps yours revolves around lazy mornings on the deck enjoying a coffee with friends, as you gaze out over the water. Or maybe an evening spin in the boat is more to your taste. Whatever our reasons for buying waterfront property, we need to make sure that our dreams and expectations match the reality of the property we are considering purchasing. This chapter is designed to help you "buy with awareness".

Ask yourself some broad questions to begin the process of clarifying your goals:

- How do you wish to use the property?
- How much and what type of space do you require for outdoor activities? Is the property big enough?
- If there is a building, do you plan on expanding, remodelling or rebuilding in the future?
- Will you be using the property seasonally or year-round?
- Do you want to be close to neighbours or secluded?
- If it is a rural property: how close to a town (shopping, medical services) do you wish to be?

Dreams…

tip Be cautious in altering your land until you get to know it. Then gradually alter it to suit your needs. It is much harder to restore land that has already been altered substantially.

Decide which factors are most important for you, and keep these as your core criteria. Narrow your search to properties that conform, *in their present state*, to as many of these factors as possible. Does the lay of the land, and the nature of the waterfront, suit your ideas? If you buy a lot where you have to convert nature in order to meet your dream, you will be taking on a major "maintenance" job – one that could be frustrating and costly.

Here are some possible dreams you might have, and some suggestions about what to consider in a shoreline property.

Your dream	Look for a property...
Open views	…where trees have already been cleared, rather than buying a treed lot and then having to clear. Leave the treed lot for those people who enjoy the feel of a cosy cabin in the woods.
Sandy beach	…with a naturally occurring beach. You'll end up frustrated if you buy a property with cattails and bulrushes on the shoreline and try to convert it – or if your beach erodes away because it was imported.
Tidy yard	…big enough to allow you to have the yard close to the house, and let the rest of the lot, especially the area alongside the water, be natural. Edges of streams, lakes and wetlands need to be undisturbed. When you "clean" a stream or a shoreline, you harm it.
Easy road access	…with shallow grades, rather than a steep one where you will have to carve up the lot with switchbacks, and risk erosion of soil.
Motorized water sports	…with a minimum-impact water access already constructed, shared access nearby, or the potential for access with minimum damage to the shore.
Room for guests	…where development or renovation is legally possible (zoning, permits, setbacks), with adequately sized services like water and sewage treatment for the extra numbers.

Hot Real Estate Markets

"Hot" markets, situations where the supply of waterfront properties is low and the prices therefore high, can mean that you are forced to move quickly into making an offer to purchase. In these circumstances, you may not wish to make your offer conditional on some of the inspections that we recommend on the next page and in other sections of the book. This could have serious consequences for you. In such cases, take a risk assessment approach; this will at least allow you to embark on your purchase with your eyes open. It's your choice, and your risk!

Use the information in this book (paying special attention to *Appendix 4* and the various *Tips for Purchasers*) to identify which features of the property could be potentially problematic. You will need to decide how much time and money you are prepared to spend on the features of your property which have a risk associated with them. In our experience, the most frequent problem areas are associated with septic systems, drinking water, shoreline erosion, and old cabins "dressed up" to look good.

Then you can decide whether the potential problems – and the costs to resolve them – are within your acceptable tolerance range. In this way you minimize the chances of nasty surprises after you've purchased. The old axiom "caveat emptor" (buyer beware) seems to apply especially to shoreline property purchase!

...Reality Check

Once you have narrowed your search and found some properties to evaluate more thoroughly, you'll need to ask extra questions. The unique characteristics of shoreline property mean that you may need to probe a little more deeply.

- Ask for photos showing the property throughout the year. Examine both the shoreline and the area above high water in these photos. Where are the water levels?
- Look at the property from all angles. Take a video or lots of photos for later.
- Research road access: if you are in doubt, find out who owns the road and who maintains it. Check for easements.
- Check whether there are covenants on the property affecting the shoreline (for example, flood plain covenants, or restrictive covenants protecting natural qualities).
- Are there culverts, creeks or runoff which drain onto the property? These could carry runoff and pollutants onto your property, and possibly pose a flood risk.
- Check that on-site sewage treatment and water systems are adequate, and meet current standards. Your financial institution may ask for proof; plus, you probably would like to avoid the costs and inconvenience of repairs, or litigation due to problems elsewhere caused by a failed sewage treatment system.
- Check with your local municipality that development on the property conforms to local zoning bylaws. Also research any special regulations which apply only to shoreline development. Are your ideas compatible with the local municipality's long-term development objectives for the area?
- You may wish to have a survey carried out, or ask the seller to provide a real property report, to make sure that the buildings are actually located on the land that you are considering purchasing. If structures encroach onto adjacent lands, such as an environmental reserve, you may need an agreement with the municipality.
- If you are considering a purchase offer, ask your realtor for the Alberta Rural or Urban Residential Property Disclosure Statement which is completed by the seller. This document outlines what the seller knows about various aspects of the property and its buildings.

⚠️ **CAUTION: *We strongly suggest that you ask additional questions about the property,*** using the Checklist in Appendix 4 as a guide, and that you make these documents all part of your "Contract of Purchase and Sale". We also strongly recommend full disclosure statements for private sales of shoreline property.

Other questions

Seasonal cycles can be experienced more intensely on a property beside water. Along with the delights of spring may come risks of flooding and runoff, while in summer you may experience drought and low water. Before developing or making major alterations to your land, learn as much as you can about its natural cycles. This way, your plans will work with your land and you might save yourself time and money in the long run.

If you have any doubt about property stability, consider hiring a hydrogeologist or soil bioengineer to provide a site-specific assessment of shoreline stability and erosion potential. *See Chapter 8.*

Do some research about the area:

- Talk to neighbours to find out what you can about the area, including the water body. Is there heavy recreational use of the water during the summer? How is it used, and is this compatible with your own preferred activities? If you are considering property with a stream on it, what are stream flows like?
- Research water levels. What is the historic 100 year flood level, and where are buildings in relation to it? What will happen to the property if lake levels and river flows change?
- Contact groups that might have done some research on the water body – for example, streamkeepers, lake groups, fish and game or naturalist clubs.
- Find out the characteristics of the area. Is there local industry or agriculture? You may find your enjoyment of the property is influenced by activities which produce dust, are noisy early in the morning or at night, spray manure, chemicals or pesticides, or produce odours.

💧 ***Check flood plain restrictions and required building setbacks. You may have trouble obtaining flood insurance if a building is on a flood plain.***

Did you know . . .
Some older waterside properties, especially in recreational areas, may be "legal non-conforming". They may be built too close to the water, or inadequately serviced with sewage treatment, for current standards. Check whether you'll be able to obtain permits for building improvements.

💧 ***Consider making an offer to purchase conditional on inspection of any elements you have doubts about – the home itself, dock, septic system, well, drinking water quality, or erosion risk.***

Did you know . . .
Covenants and easements are often a fact of life with shoreline property. Sloping land, access, and environmental protection often mean extra legal requirements.

💧 ***Before you buy, evaluate how the property might change on a seasonal basis, as a result of influences like runoff and changing water levels.***

③ The Buffer Zone

Your Problem Solver

When we moved from the city to the water's edge, our plan was to live slower lives and enjoy the things that nature, and our new community, had to offer. Somehow, things worked out a little differently! Our time and resources were stretched to the limit with running a resort, keeping our consulting business going, and trying to find time to spend with the children. We welcomed anything that could save us time or prevent future problems – such as the concept of the buffer zone.

If there is one single message that every one of us who lives beside water, or has water running through our property, can benefit from, it is the value of the "buffer zone", and the importance of protecting it. The buffer zone is an excellent investment for maintaining the quality of your water and protecting your land, possibly even from disappearing!

Your buffer zone is an area of natural vegetation, including fallen trees, branches and washed up logs, and natural rocks or pebbles, that runs along the length of your shoreline, streamside, or bluff edge. It includes the areas upland of the high water mark (your **riparian** buffer) as well as the area below the high water mark right down into the water (your **aquatic** buffer).

Ideally, a buffer zone contains vegetation that would normally grow in your area, based on climatic zone and physical location. These might include trees, shrubs, wildflowers, grasses and other plants in the riparian area, and native aquatic plants (like cattails and rushes).

What's in a Name?

The riparian buffer zone has many other names – buffer strip, leave strip, filter strip, riparian zone, and vegetation retention zone. Some call it the ribbon of life, because of its crucial role for many living things.

Over the years, many of us have cleared our buffers for views, created wide access swaths to the shore, and "tidied" up the shoreline. Lawns and ornamental gardens near the water's edge, artificial beaches, retaining walls and other "hard" installations along many shorelines have gradually eliminated the ability of buffers to function effectively.

When a shoreline is cleared and native vegetation removed along with logs, rocks and boulders, the buffer area has the potential to become an "erosion zone". Alterations to shorelines and streambanks can also result in silted-up spawning beds, pollution from runoff and increased flooding. By helping buffers return to a more natural state, we can often reduce these problems.

As "pollution-prevention, water quality control, and erosion-protection devices", riparian and aquatic buffers help keep our property and water safe. In fact, you could look at them as a free shoreline insurance program...we invite you to take advantage of this opportunity!

⚠ **CAUTION**
Without a buffer zone you might find that your shoreline becomes an erosion zone. You then risk:
• **Physical loss of your property.**
• **Civil litigation from neighbours if their property is damaged.**
• **Possible criminal charges if fish habitat is harmed or destroyed.**

Finding Your Buffer Zone

Your buffer zone includes vegetation along the water's edge adapted for the environment there – plants that like the extra moisture. The area above the high water mark which is influenced by the presence of water – for example, seeping through the soil – is the "riparian" area. Adjacent to the riparian area is the "upland". Your riparian buffer zone will include all of the riparian area, and often includes some upland area.

Vegetation and soils will help you identify your riparian buffer. Some riparian buffers may lack trees and shrubs, even in a natural state, due to characteristics such as soils which may be too wet. And, some aquatic buffers may naturally lack emergent aquatic vegetation like rushes and submergent plants growing in the water. Rocks, fallen trees, and washed up logs also act as part of your buffer.

Did you know...
Buffer zones provide rich and important habitat for fish and other wildlife. Scientists say that natural habitat ABOVE the high water mark is very important to the survival of many species of fish.

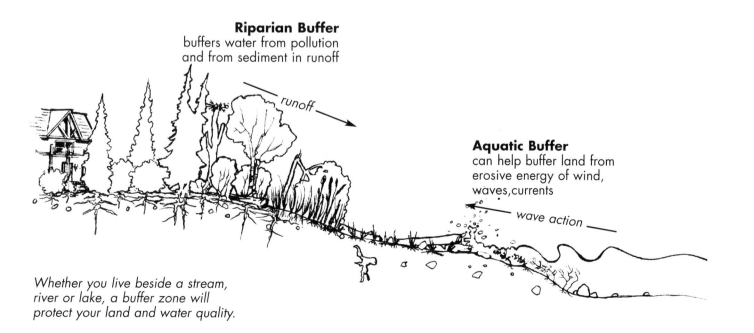

Riparian Buffer
buffers water from pollution and from sediment in runoff

runoff

Aquatic Buffer
can help buffer land from erosive energy of wind, waves, currents

wave action

Whether you live beside a stream, river or lake, a buffer zone will protect your land and water quality.

The Benefits of Buffers

Benefit	How buffers help

Protection of water quality	• Buffers help purify water by filtering toxic substances and some pollutants (fertilizers, pesticides, bacteria, heavy metals and septic leachate) out of runoff from roads, fields, yards and septic fields, before these substances reach water bodies.
	• Vegetation helps keep water clear by trapping soil particles in runoff.
	• On a property with extensive native vegetation, you can avoid the use of fertilizers and pesticides and further help protect water quality; these substances are not required to grow native plants.
	• If properly established and maintained, a full riparian buffer can remove at least: - 50 percent of chemical fertilizers and pesticides.
	     - 60 percent of some bacteria.
	     - 75 percent of sediment.

Protection from erosion	• The roots of riparian and aquatic buffer vegetation act like "rebar" in concrete, to reinforce soil and sand and help hold them together. • Buffers help prevent land loss by protecting your bank or shoreline from slumping or being washed away. • The leaves of plants reduce the energy of waves and currents, break the force of falling rain, and slow water as it runs downhill. Since shoreline properties are commonly on the receiving end of drainage, the more vegetation cover, the more your property will benefit.
Protection of property value	• By protecting water quality and preventing erosion along the shoreline, a buffer zone helps maintain the value of your property. • Buffers help protect buildings and trees on your property from damage due to wind and water.
Protection from flooding	• Vegetation, logs and rocks in streams or along the shoreline slow down flood waters, reducing damage to your property. • Riparian vegetation acts like a sponge, helping to increase the soil's ability to absorb water, and to lessen the impacts of flooding.
Quality of life	• Trees and other vegetation provide cooling and shade in summer, protection from wind in winter, and they clean and freshen the air. • Vegetation along the shoreline can provide privacy from other dwellings and from noisy activities on the water. • Natural landscaping can help put you in touch with the seasonal cycles of plants and wildlife, and the beauty of nature.
Protection of water supply	• Riparian vegetation helps the ground absorb more water in fall, winter and spring, and during storms. The ground can then slowly release water into streams in the summer, to help maintain flows during dry periods.
Protection of fish and wildlife	• Vegetation provides food, nesting cover, and shelter for fish and other wildlife, including species-at-risk. • Vegetation alongside and overhanging waterways provides shade to help keep water cool for fish. • Vegetation along shorelines provides connecting corridors, enabling wildlife to move safely from one area to another.

" A few of us on our lake have brought in sand for beaches. If I had realized that it would silt over the gravel area where trout used to spawn, I wouldn't have done it – and I'm sure my neighbours wouldn't have either. "

Shoreline resident

What Makes an Effective Buffer?

Native plants... and lots of them!

Ideally, the buffer area is thickly covered with native vegetation. The higher the percentage of the ground that is covered, the better your buffer can work. A landscape made up of native plants is low-maintenance. Once established, they can survive without extra watering, and without application of pesticides and fertilizers. Native plants are adapted to deal with local bugs and diseases and can get all the nutrients they need from existing soil. *See Chapter 7 and Appendix 2 for more information on native plants.* A ground covering of turf grass does not provide enough of the functions of a buffer to be effective.

The wider the better!

Scientists are showing us that buffer zones need to be much wider than previously thought, in order for them to carry out all the functions that nature intends for them. These days, the general rule for an effective riparian buffer is to provide a minimum width of 30 m (100 ft), measured inland from the high water line. You may also need to increase the size of your buffer if you live on a ravine or sloped shoreline or if the shore or bank is made of rock. *See sidebar.*

In addition to the riparian buffer, some shorelines also have an aquatic buffer, particularly lakes. In some areas, riparian buffer zones as wide as 50-100 m (165-330 ft) may be established, to help protect very sensitive stream shorelines. In exceptionally fragile areas, 150 m (500 ft) may be required. The buffer is often set aside by the municipality as an environmental reserve and strict guidelines apply.

Wide buffers are best at filtering out pollutants before they reach the water, protecting soil from eroding, mitigating the effects of flooding, and providing habitat for fish and other wildlife.

If you have a lot which has already been cleared, if your lot is too small to establish the buffer we recommend, or if your house or cottage is closer than 30 m (100 ft) to the water's edge – you may feel that the task of creating a buffer is irrelevant, or impossible for you. Do not despair! Whatever you set aside for a natural buffer area along the shoreline will benefit your property. Start slowly, and the rewards may inspire you to expand the area.

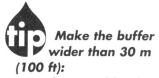

tip *Make the buffer wider than 30 m (100 ft):*
– on slopes: add at least 0.6 m for every 1 percent of slope. See Pg 71 for calculating slope.
– if rock outcrops are included, or wetlands are adjacent: add the width of the outcrop/ wetland.

Did you know . . . *Leaving a buffer strip does not mean that you will be inundated with insects, mice, skunks or other wildlife. If wildlife can find what they need on your shoreline, they will probably stay there – unless you invite them with tasty dinners of garbage, or warm inviting beds for the winter. See Chapter 11.*

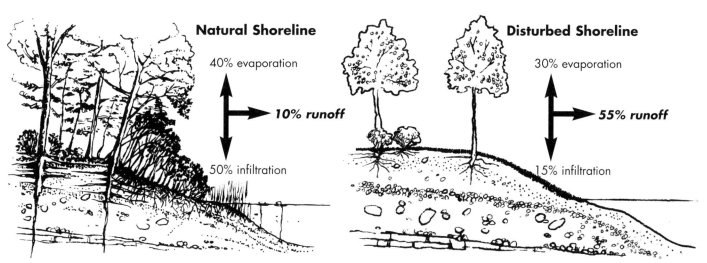

Natural Shoreline
40% evaporation
10% runoff
50% infiltration

Disturbed Shoreline
30% evaporation
55% runoff
15% infiltration

Native vegetation protects water quality from polluted runoff, and helps soil absorb water.

Hard surfaces and reduced vegetation increase runoff and and erosion potential, and decrease absorption by the soil.

> *By letting a wide buffer strip grow along the water's edge we've cut down on our yard maintenance. Each year we see tiny new shrubs popping through the ground, and have fewer worries about the water being damaged by septic leachate and runoff.*
>
> Sarah and Clive

Did you know . . .

Wetlands provide breeding, nesting and wintering habitat for thousands of migratory birds, as well as habitat for many other species of wildlife.

Variety...the spice of life

An effective buffer mimics the complexity of nature. Vegetation of different heights, types, and ages grows all mixed together. In a healthy natural shoreline, new saplings crowd up next to their parent tree, rotting wood from fallen trees provides nutrients for new grasses and shrubs, and cover for young fish. Tall plants provide shade and protection for smaller ones and, as they die, make room for new ones to grow. All this framework, both above and below ground, acts like a skeleton, holding the structure of your shoreline together.

An effective buffer generally has a mix of different types of plants, ranging from low-growing grasses, flowers, ferns and other plants to shrubs and trees of various heights. Plants with deep, binding root masses help hold the shoreline together. There may be some standing dead trees, signifying that the buffer is renewing itself. Note that some soils (such as very wet or sandy soils) may not support the full variety of vegetation described here, but the buffer can still be healthy and functioning.

In the aquatic buffer, shoreline plants such as grasses, reeds and cattails, other emergent plants such as water lilies and submergent plants such as coontail and pondweed (what we often call water weeds) bind the soil, break the force of waves, and function as a collective kidney, filtering pollutants and purifying the water. Remember though, that they, like us, can only cope with a certain level of toxins; overdosed, they can die!

Don't bare your soil!

Any bare ground we create – by paving a boat access, importing sand for a beach, or using a path until there is no vegetation left – decreases the effectiveness of our buffer. And when we harden our shoreline with retaining walls or solid docks, we can severely interfere with the buffer's ability to work. *See Chapters 7 and 8.*

Beware alien invaders

Invasive plants ("alien invaders"), discussed in Chapter 7, have the potential to interfere with the functions that a buffer performs. A healthy functioning buffer is free of them.

Wetlands

Wetlands are an important element of your property that need buffering and protection, just as much as a lake. A healthy wetland, like a healthy shoreline, safeguards your water supply through filtration and by replenishing groundwater, and plays a vital role in the survival of many species of amphibians, reptiles, water birds, mammals and specialized plants.

All wetlands have three things in common – water, water-saturated soils and water-tolerant plants. Wetlands combine features of both land and water.

Wetlands tend to develop in places where water collects and remains at or near the surface, and they can range from small depressions that hold water only after spring runoff, to forested swamps with saturated peat soils. They can be found beside streams and lakes, as well as low lying areas. If you have them along your shoreline, they will be part of your aquatic buffer.

Nurturing Your Buffer

Restoring a buffer

If your buffer zone has been altered by years of human occupation, it is possible to restore some of its natural functions. You can start small by leaving it alone and letting nature take over; if you maintain a lawn to the water's edge, stop mowing the area along the shore. Through time, your turf grass will grow longer, and native plants from surrounding areas will gradually move in. You can speed things up by removing turf and planting nursery stock. If your shoreline is eroding, of course, you'll need to take more direct action using a careful, planned approach. Chapters 7 and 8 provide planting tips and suggestions for softening a hardened shoreline and for dealing with erosion. Look for the Shoreline Restoration icon in these chapters.

Because you are working to create something that nature would have created in the first place, your work will be easier. You'll find new plants springing up, and if you leave them alone, chances are they'll thrive and spread over time. Gradually, a mix of plants of different ages will develop, and your property will reap the benefits of the buffer.

> ⚠ **CAUTION:** *A reminder – you'll need to watch out for "alien invaders"* See Chapter 7 and Appendix 2.

When you start the process of restoring a buffer area, make sure that you consider your own needs for access, recreation, and views, as well as what the buffer requires to function effectively. In this way you'll have a design you can live with.

Building on your land

In Chapter 4 we give tips for construction, and for protecting your buffer when clearing a building site. Leave the edge of the buffer uneven with a mix of plant heights and types, and clusters of vegetation. This kind of variety helps provide lots of fallen leaves, needles and twigs to slow water runoff and encourage absorption. It also provides useful habitat for birds and small mammals looking for food and shelter.

Accessing the water

In Chapter 9 we suggest ideas for minimizing buffer damage when you create access to the water's edge, by creating the smallest possible "puncture" in your buffer. Try to keep as much of your shoreline untouched as possible, and focus your access pathway and other activities in one general area. On steep shorelines, any access may cause instability, and you may need to look at alternate ways of reaching the water, such as using a nearby public dock.

Where have I heard that before....?

As you read this book, you may notice that maintaining or restoring a buffer zone is a common theme repeated throughout. This is because the benefits of the buffer relate to many areas of waterfront living: shoreline landscaping, erosion control, water quality, construction, septic systems, hobby farming, recreation, wildlife, natural beauty.... the list goes on. Protect your water, your investment in your property, and your health. Nurture your buffer and save yourself time, headaches, and money.

tip *Metre by metre... yard by yard.* **Show your buffer to your neighbours. Re-establishing buffer zones is something we can each contribute to, a metre at a time and one yard at a time!**

CAUTION
Shorelines, especially those beside fast currents and banks, bluffs, cliffs and rocky areas, can be dangerous places. Take all necessary precautions whenever you are planting or doing any other work in hazardous areas.

Resources

Caring For Shoreline Properties: Changing the Way We Look at Owning Lakefront Property in Alberta. 1999. Valastin, Pat. Alberta Conservation Association. Edmonton, Alberta.

The Shore Primer: A Cottager's Guide to a Healthy Waterfront. Fisheries and Oceans Canada. www.dfo-mpo.gc.ca/publications/Shore%20Primer_e.pdf

Lakescaping for Wildlife and Water Quality. 2000. Henderson, Carrol L. et al. Department of Natural Resources. St. Paul, Minnesota.

See Appendix 1 for complete Resources.

Treat your shoreline like the delicate treasure that it is...not just another frontage to be cleared and readied for construction.

Working With Your Land

④ Construction Projects

Protecting Your Property

A few years ago a neighbour built a shop on his property, to move his business out of his house. When he was clearing the site for the footings, he noticed a wet area and installed drainage to route the moisture away from his building. As soon as he had excavated and poured the footings for the shop, our neighbour discovered, to his horror, that his well was losing pressure. He has never been able to restore it. He figures that the wet area fed his well, and his construction project interfered with the water flow. Since then, he has had to haul water.

We think of buildings as improvements to our property. However, any building project, small or large, also has the potential to damage your shoreline and reduce your property's appeal. Your waterfront or streamside property has unique characteristics – take them into account when planning your building project! This holds true for large projects like a house, and for smaller ones like a deck or gazebo. Plan wisely to avoid costly problems. These can include cracked foundations, wet crawl spaces or basements, recurring annoyances such as lingering sewage odours, a building threatened by an eroding shoreline or, as our neighbour found, a redirected water flow. Build to protect the stability of your shoreline, and to keep your water clean for fishing, wildlife, and perhaps swimming and drinking. The tips in this section will help you protect both the investment in your project, and your land. They may also save you some time and money!

Big or small, take the time to plan

Before you engage a professional advisor, hire a contractor, or start ordering materials, take a few minutes to read this chapter, and even more time to plan.

Consider special features of your land and its microclimate when you choose your building site and develop your construction plans. You may be able to place your buildings in ways that make them more energy efficient and more comfortable. Factors such as localized breezes, frost pockets, and daytime and nighttime wind flow can all affect your project. Also consider the effect of seasonal cycles: spring runoff, winter storms, and snow pack.

⚠ **CAUTION: *Don't let your contractor or professional advisor talk you into clearing your lot as if it was a typical suburban development.*** It's too dangerous a practice and could turn your shoreline into an "erosion zone"! Nature's approach to protecting your shoreline is cost efficient and low maintenance!

Planning Your Project

Preparing a site plan

Preparing a site plan is a useful exercise for learning about your property and its natural features. It will help you plan both construction and landscaping projects. If you can, obtain an air photo of your property; features such as drainage patterns can be identified more easily.

- Check with your municipality for local zoning regulations and development permit requirements, before beginning any landscaping or construction, even for a gazebo or a sauna. Many municipalities establish environmental reserves along the water or require minimum setbacks. Your plan must conform.

  ⚠ **CAUTION: *You could lose both time and money if you choose to ignore regulations.*** These days there are many eyes on your shoreline, including those of your neighbours, by-law enforcement and fisheries officers.

- Identify areas for services like septic and wells, and environmentally sensitive features like wetlands and rare trees. Then select possible building sites.

- Locate roads and driveways to minimize the risk of erosion. Ease of access will guide your choice of building site. Evaluate whether you could share a common entrance off the main road with a neighbour to reduce the length of drive that you build, and save on construction costs.

- Show how you intend to handle drainage from rain and snow-melt. Identify potential unprotected slopes susceptible to erosion, and drainage areas where runoff can be directed. *See Pg 23.*

1. Understand the natural features and processes unique to your property and choose building sites and designs which are compatible.

2. Locate your high water mark and check for any floodplain or environmental covenants or easements. *See Chapter 17.*

3. Check with your municipality for local zoning regulations, development permit requirements and minimum setbacks from water.

4. Site your well and septic system first, and identify any environmentally sensitive areas such as wetlands to protect.

5. Choose a building site requiring minimal clearing of trees and shrubs, as far back from the shore as possible (minimum 30 m/100 ft), farther back on steep sites or where special regulations require.

6. If possible leave a buffer strip of natural vegetation at least 30 m (100 ft) wide along the shoreline. Keep well back from edges of bluffs and crests of ravines.

7. Focus alterations like a path, dock or boat launch in one area of your shoreline. Leave as much as possible natural.

8. Plan roads and driveways to minimize site clearing and erosion.

9. Divert and slow the flow of rainwater and snow melt to prevent moisture and erosion problems.

10. Obtain views of the water through pruning and limbing trees, rather than felling.

11. Build to discourage wildlife from sharing your home. In return, consider enhancing wildlife habitat elsewhere on your property.

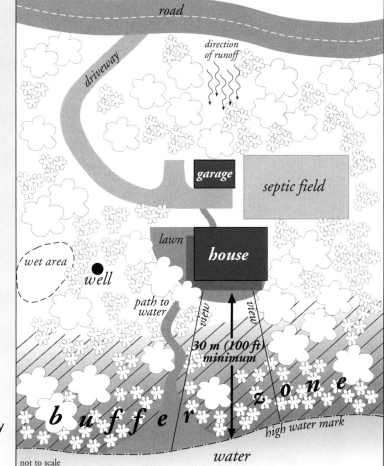

Sample site plan

tip *Retain existing native plants on your property for a low maintenance landscape. You will help protect your shoreline from erosion, your water from pollution, and maintain natural wildlife habitat.*

We built our cottage in a sheltered spot against the bank. We couldn't understand why it always seemed to have a musty smell. One spring we dug a trench around it for drainage. The trench filled with water. Apparently water had been seeping out of the bank and under the cottage floor for years.

Shoreline resident

Did you know ..

When you leave only a few of the original trees on your property, you expose them to blowdown risk. The trees growing together in a stand are interdependent; when some of them are removed, the remainder are weakened.

Assessing ground conditions

Building on the wrong surface can lead to environmental and health hazards as a result of damp basements, flooding, erosion, or poor septic drainfield function. *See Chapter 5.*

- Site your services first – your well and septic system (if relevant).
- Check the ground quality at your chosen sites; it may be too wet for your building project if you see any of the following:
  - The ground is soft and spongy even if it hasn't rained in a while.
  - The proposed site is at the base of a bank, in a depression, or is not significantly higher than nearby water.
  - Plants like horsetails, rushes, sedges, and cattails, or trees such as willow, birch or cottonwood grow nearby.

If your soil is dry (very sandy, or "fluffy"), you will need to take extra precautions to avoid erosion problems during and after construction. *See Pg 27.*

Utilizing existing trees and shrubs

Choose a site requiring minimal clearing of trees and shrubs. Pay special attention to protecting the vegetation growing along your shoreline. If you live on a bluff overlooking a large lake, remember that even the most scraggly tree is doing its part to protect trees behind from the full force of winds.

- Maintain a thick buffer of shrubs and trees (preferably native) between you and the water. *See Chapter 7 and Appendix 2 for further information on native plants.* Keeping your shoreline buffer, with trees and shrubs of varying ages, will provide privacy, absorb noise, protect your shoreline from erosion, filter runoff, and provide wildlife habitat.
- Consider clearing small "rooms" in your shrub and forest areas to create spaces for recreational activities. Instead of removing a stand of trees, try removing just a few.

- Identify any specific trees (such as mature trees or rare species) on your property that you definitely want to protect. Plan your design around them. If you work near these trees, protect them from damage during construction. *See Pg 27.*
- Also identify and protect any sensitive areas such as a wetland, an area of unusual vegetation, or nesting areas for shore or water birds.

The lay of the land

Understand natural processes operating on your property and choose building sites and designs which are compatible.

Building near bluffs

Many of us are tempted to build near bluffs to obtain views over the water. Remember, a bluff is prone to erosion. It may look stable now but sometimes clearing your building site, changing drainage patterns or putting the extra weight of a building near the edge of the slope can increase the rate of erosion and add to the risk of slumpage.

In general, farther back is better. A 30 m (100 ft) setback may seem like a large distance, but for a bluff that is eroding at the rate of 60 cm (24 in) a year, in thirty years your building will only be 12 m (40 ft) from the edge of the bluff!

Site drainage

Waterfront properties tend to be on the receiving end of surface runoff and underground seepage. Evaluate the natural drainage patterns on your site and protect natural drainage ways such as gullies or low areas. Choose building sites that will minimize interference with these.

A plan for dealing with runoff, especially peak water flow during storms and spring time, will protect your property from:

- Erosion caused or worsened by surface runoff and groundwater seepage.
- Loss of valuable soil.
- Water pollution from sediments, fertilizers and chemicals in runoff. *See Pg 22.*

Building location

Determine where sunlight falls on your land during different seasons and at different times of the day. This may help save you money on heating and cooling bills.

- Choose a site which is sheltered from the prevailing wind.
- Choose a site which provides shelter from winter cold and summer heat. Consider earth-sheltered, or partially earth-sheltered, designs where the land is sloping. Earth-sheltered houses benefit from the soil's summer coolness and its relative warmth in the winter.
- Choose a position that allows for maximum winter sunlight, to save on heating bills.
- Keep deciduous trees on your home's western and southern exposure; they will provide shade in the summer and allow sunlight to enter in the winter. Evergreens on northern exposures give shelter from winter winds.
- Take advantage of downslope breezes for natural cooling when planning your building layout and window configuration. On most large bodies of water, daytime breezes move from water to land; night breezes move from land to water.

Enhancing views

One of the best things about living by the water is the view! By planning carefully, we can create view "corridors" that give us all the spectacular scenery we need and still leave our shoreline buffer intact. This also protects the view from the water that studies say many people prefer – well vegetated shorelines with buildings hidden from view.

- Protect native trees, shrubs, and grasses between your home and the water.
- Prune or limb trees and shrubs, instead of removing them, to permit views of water. This also helps maintain your privacy. A skilled arborist can identify what limbs will open up views, sometimes with dramatic results. *See Chapter 7 for pruning tips.*

- Plan window locations to take advantage of views that already exist, rather than using an "off-the-shelf" building design and then clearing vegetation to create view corridors.
- To help your house blend in when seen from the water, use natural building materials like wood and stone, and natural colours for shingles and paints. Dark colours recede into the background and are less obtrusive than light colours.
- If having people see your house from the water is important to you, limb trees to open up views. This helps protect your buffer and keeps your options open should you want more privacy in the future.
- Create meandering paths and trails to screen buildings from view.
- Screen outbuildings, swing sets, barbecues, and fuel tanks with vegetation.
- Consider creepers or vines on a trellis for added camouflage on buildings.
- Carefully plan the location of outdoor lighting. Shade lights with overhangs to focus the light down, rather than out to water or to your neighbours. Install motion or heat sensor lights and use yellow bulbs.

« When planning projects during the winter months, it is easy to forget how hot it can get on an exposed beach. The many trees in our buffer provide great shade for our sitting area. »

Shoreline resident

Did you know...

Your property may come with its own unique microclimate. Features like a meadow, a steep slope, or a stand of trees can lead to localized winds, and pockets of colder or warmer air. Observe your microclimate to determine the best design and location of your new structure.

Prune or limb trees instead of removing them to open up views of the water.

Build to keep small critters out of your home by filling tiny access points around plumbing and electrical outlets. Get your contractor to pay attention to detail or you will be fighting a losing battle trying to destroy small mammals and insects.

Did you know . . .

Most waterfront property slopes down to water. Sloping land poses extra challenges for construction, managing runoff, road building, septic fields – even for walking trails.

" Though we were careful with detail, we discovered that insects were entering our new house. Wasps were getting into a tiny space in the soffit around the deck's light fixture. Later we found that ants were entering through a gap that the plumber hadn't caulked after installing a direct vent gas fireplace. "

Sarah & Clive

Living with wildlife

Build carefully to discourage wildlife from sharing your home with you. In return, maintain and enhance wildlife habitat elsewhere on your property. *See Chapter 11 for tips.*

- Evaluate your site at different seasons, and different times of day, to learn about wildlife patterns. Is there a frequented watering hole, a wildlife corridor, a breeding area, or sensitive wildlife habitat on your land? If so, consider avoiding this area. You will reduce unwanted encounters with wildlife in your home, and protect areas that are important for them.

- Animal proof your home whether you are building new or retrofitting. Pay attention to detail, but use simple solutions.

- Emphasize to your contractor the critical importance of proper sealing. For example, caulk on the outside of any gas or water pipes, electrical conduit, TV or phone cables, or exhaust vents that pass through the wall. Make sure outside trim is fitted snugly against windows and doors, and adjoining finishes such as siding or stucco, but do not caulk these from the outside. Before drywall is installed, use acoustic sealant to seal horizontal framing members where plumbing and other cables pass through, to prevent runways from basement to attic.

- Fill any gaps between the concrete foundation and walls and install drywall tight to the floor. Although carpets and trim will hide these joints, insects and rodents can still get in.

Fill all access points to keep insects and small mammals out of your house.

- On exteriors, make sure there are no gaps in the soffit through which wasps or other insects can enter to build nests.

- For wood doors, make sure that your door seals are properly fitted.

Dealing with moisture

Excess moisture seeping into your building can mean potential for rot, cracked foundations and musty odours.

- Drainage tile is required around all building foundations in Alberta. If you suspect that site drainage may be an issue, talk to your contractor about enhancing your drainage system.

- Use good quality latex paints and stains.

- For decks, stain the top, bottom, sides and cut ends of your lumber before building the deck.

Managing site drainage

Most waterfront properties have some degree of surface and groundwater flow. Although you may never be able to control these water flows entirely, you can do your best to manage them so they are not contributing to accelerated erosion and landslides along your waterfront. Some ideas:

- Minimize paved and other hard surface areas such as patios. For paths and sitting areas, use gravel, small modular paving stones, flagstones, decay-resistant wood blocks, or pre-fabricated concrete lattice (filled with soil and seeded). Small paving stones and concrete lattices provide durability while allowing rainwater and snowmelt to filter into the ground – either through them, or between joints. Avoid paving areas that will serve no useful function.

- Use swales (gentle depressions in a slope), berms (low ridges), gravel filled trenches or other methods to redirect water.

- Design your drainage system to slow surface runoff water, with curves (lined with rocks if necessary) and settling pools. This will also give sediment a chance to settle out. Avoid straight ditches that head directly for the water.

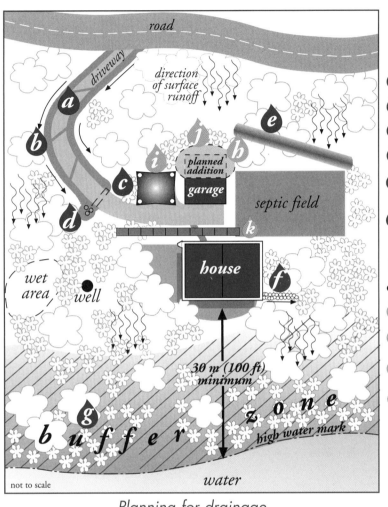

Planning for drainage

a driveway
water bars

b runoff ditches

c culvert

d settling pool for
driveway runoff

e depression
(swale) redirects
surface runoff

f roof runoff
directed in gravel-
filled trench

g buffer zone
filters runoff

construction tips

h clear minimum
area for project

i cover excavated
soil with tarp

j replant cleared
area promptly

k filter runoff
with silt fencing
or straw bales

tip *Before you build,
check your site in the
spring. If there is strong
underground seepage in
the area, either look for
alternative locations that
are drier or, if you must
build there, install a double
weeping tile system.*

The 4 D's of Runoff Control

Decrease the amount
of runoff you cause.
Detain water to slow it down.
Divert the runoff to less
erodible areas.
Dissipate the runoff –
spread it out.

Did you know ...

*The biggest
impact on streams from
runoff is from paving over
lots, roads and parking
areas. Make your lot as
permeable to rain as possible, by using alternate
groundcovers to turf grass
and minimizing other hard
surfaces.*

- Direct downspouts from eavestroughing to discharge where soil will not be eroded. Provide erosion protection (like splash pads and/or a trench filled with drain rock) where the downspout discharges, or link it to your weeping tile system if it discharges on your land.

- Wherever possible, keep existing natural vegetation or enhance it with native landscaping.

- Never discharge a drainage pipe at the top of a ravine, bluff or bank.

- Work with your neighbours to create a mutually satisfactory plan for handling runoff. Avoid having your runoff spill onto their property and you will avoid a potential neighbourly dispute!

Even if your circumstances require major shoreline stabilization efforts, dealing with your site's drainage is essential to control erosion. *See Chapter 8 for more information on shoreline stabilization.*

*Direct water from eaves-
troughs into a rock-filled
trench or dry well.*

Install water bars across driveway to divert runoff.

Driveways surfaced with gravel result in less runoff than paved surfaces. If you minimize the number and size of paved areas you create, the ground will absorb more rainfall and runoff will be reduced.

tip **Reduce the amount of dust and dirt getting into your house from your driveway by:**
- **Having a mud room or covered porch with boot scrapers and mats.**
- **Replacing entrance mats when dirty or worn.**
- **Minimizing the amount of soil exposed on your site and retaining native vegetation.**

Planning driveways and paths

Plan the driveway to your house carefully. Steep driveways can damage the land, are susceptible to erosion and slumping, provide an easy route for silt-laden runoff to the water and are difficult in wet or icy conditions. While many of us want to be as close to the water as possible, you may find after reviewing the following factors that it makes more sense for you to build farther back from the water's edge, or to keep your vehicles closer to your main road. *See Chapter 9 for accessing the water for boating.*

Design

- Keep the driveway as far from surface water as possible to keep sand, gravel and road salt out of runoff.
- Plan for construction and emergency vehicle access.
- Include a turn-around or pull-out in your design, as well as parking for your visitors.
- Plan for snow:
  - If your grade is steep, include a winter parking option in your design.
  - If possible, orient your road to take advantage of the sun, so that it thaws more quickly.
  - If you plough your drive rather than snowblow it, identify suitable open areas for the plough to push the snow to avoid damaging trees and shrubs.
  - Remember that drifting snow accumulates on the leeward side of windbreaks such as fences and hedges. Plan your driveway to avoid such areas.

Plan for road drainage

- Plan for drainage; to prevent erosion from runoff, follow the contours of your land.
  - Angle roads across the hill's gradient; driveways that cut straight downhill give water too much of a running start.
- Use porous materials for road surfaces, such as gravel, small modular pavers, or pre-cast concrete lattice.
- Divert runoff and drainage into areas that can absorb it, away from surface water.
  - Install water bars (runoff logs) at frequent intervals along the length of your driveway or road. They prevent runoff from becoming too concentrated. Landscaping ties are inexpensive and work well. For a driveway that is already paved, consider adding "speed bumps" that also help to divert runoff.
  - Use roadside banks (in conjunction with water bars) as low-budget runoff deflectors.
  - Install settling pools in runoff ditches that slope to water.

Footpaths

- Plan footpaths to avoid erosion, just as you would plan road access, using slope contours and keeping trails narrow. Avoid straight runs down the slope to the water. Consider a staircase if the slope is very steep. (Make sure to incorporate landings or turns for safety.) *See Chapter 9.*

Stream crossings

If access to your proposed building site requires a stream crossing, make sure you obtain the necessary approvals from Alberta Environment.

- Cross at right angles to the stream.
- Use a size and type of culvert appropriate for the stream size, and do not block fish access. A poorly placed culvert can block a spawning stream as effectively as a multi-million dollar hydroelectric dam! An undersized culvert can result in flooding and erosion during a sudden summer rainstorm or spring runoff. Special culverts suitable for fish-bearing streams may be required.

Construction Tips

Planning to protect your property

Provide your contractor (and any professional advisors) with a thorough briefing on factors that are important to you.

⚠ **CAUTION: You'll also need to take these factors into account if you're doing the job yourself.** These may include :

* Features on your property that you want to protect:
  * your well and septic system (if relevant)
  * your buffer zone and sensitive vegetation
  * drainage areas or gullies
  * sensitive areas like wetlands or meadows
* Areas for storing construction materials
* Parking and turnaround areas for construction vehicles
* Location for a portable toilet if there is none on-site

Make a plan for protecting your property's special features and agree on methods that everyone (including the contractor and crew) will understand and recognize. Decide who will :

* Communicate your expectations to, and supervise, the subcontractors.
* Clean up materials and how often.
* Cover up bare ground to minimize erosion.
* Check on the property after a major rainstorm.

Walk the site at least twice to go over these points with your contractor, the second time having him or her relay back to you what you want carried out. The more that you put in writing, the less chance of miscommunication.

Hiring a contractor

If you hire a contractor, spend time selecting one with whom you feel comfortable. The time and effort you invest in finding the right contractor will be worth your while. Hiring someone who lacks qualifications, or with whom you have trouble communicating, can lead to confusion, frustration, and unnecessary expense for everyone. It can also result in irreparable damage to your property such as trees felled without authorization.

Word of mouth and recommendations may still be the best way to find a contractor who meets your needs. Once you have one or two names recommended, evaluate the alternatives. Use the same approach any time you hire people to advise or help you – from landscapers to engineers! *See sidebar on next page.*

Protecting your site during construction

1. Hire qualified contractors who will respect your land and your plans; use written contracts to clearly outline responsibilities and expectations.

2. Clear only the minimum area required for the project.

3. Protect trees from damage caused by digging and heavy machinery.

4. Clearly mark trees to be felled to avoid unnecessary tree removal.

5. Save and cover topsoil in a separate place when clearing.

6. To prevent erosion and protect water quality, keep bare soil covered as much as possible, and divert any dirty runoff water away from surface water.

7. Use appropriately sized machinery for the job.

8. Use the least toxic building materials available both inside and outside your home.

9. Dispose of construction debris appropriately.

10. Prevent spills of harmful materials.

11. Keep a "Green Bin" on hand to deal with any hazardous material spill that may occur.

Choosing the Right Contractor

Experience
- Length of time in business
- Experience with projects beside water – remember your property is very special

Qualifications
- Certificates and licences
- Knowledgeable about new building techniques, local regulations, etc.
- Ability to carry out the kind of project you require
- Thoroughness and ability to pay attention to detail

Reputation
- Status with your local Chamber of Commerce, local Builders' Associations, the Better Business Bureau, local professionals involved in the construction industry such as architects, developers, realtors, and local financial and legal institutions (banks, notaries or lawyers)

References
- Evaluative comments made by previous clients (e.g., responses to questions such as whether the projects were well-built and on schedule? Did they have problems? How was the contractor to work with? Did the contractor respect the natural features of their property?)

Warranty
- Willingness to warranty work
- Details of the warranty offered by the contractor
- Length of warranty

Contract details
- Use of sub-contractors
- Written contract which covers details such as deadlines, penalties for non-performance, etc.

Personality
- Ability to develop a good working relationship with you
- Degree to which your philosophies and concerns mesh

Clear the minimum area necessary for your project.

Preparing your site

Less is more.... protection for you, that is! Clear the minimum that is necessary for your project and for site access.

You may be tempted, either by a contractor or by mistakenly thinking you might save money, to clear your whole property at once. Although it may seem like effective use of your heavy equipment to do this, it could set the stage later for problems with erosion, slumping and deteriorating water quality. It may also be against the law.

If you think you need to clear your site in order to create an attractive yard, save yourself some time and money by first reviewing Chapter 7 which focusses on landscaping with existing native vegetation. There are many good resources to help in planning a landscaping design which incorporates native shrubs, trees and grasses.

The best option is to clear only what is necessary for your access drive, septic field and well access (if relevant), and building. Whatever the topography of your site, from bluff to gentle slope, protect it by leaving and maintaining a wide buffer of groundcover between the construction site and the water's edge, or bluff's crest.

⚠️ **CAUTION: *If tree felling is a necessary part of your project:***
- Plan to be on-site the day any trees are to be felled.
- Clearly mark your property boundaries especially if you have an environmental reserve between your property and the water.
- Clearly mark any trees or bushes that you wish to have removed. Make it clear that unmarked trees and bushes are staying!
- Make sure your contractor clearly understands which trees you want to protect.

While the contractor's job may be eased by tree removal, mature trees are a priceless feature that take a lifetime to grow.

Leave the stumps and root systems undisturbed on any tree that you cut on a slope (unless it is part of your septic field or building site). If you need to remove a stump, you may be able to do it with minimal disturbance using a stump grinder.

Protecting trees during construction

Trees are often damaged during construction and then die later. Major damage is caused by grade changes around trees, soil compaction, injuries such as gouging from heavy machinery, and tree thinning. The extra initial expense of careful site development to avoid these problems is a worthwhile investment.

- Use temporary fencing around trees and shrubs to protect them from damage by construction vehicles.

- Keep all digging and excavation at least 3 m (10 ft) from any tree you want to preserve. Roots generally extend to at least the ends of the branches (the "drip line").

- To avoid compacting soil around trees and cutting off air and water to roots, hand clear brush surrounding trees rather than using heavy machinery.

- Do not bury tree roots when backfilling or grading. Even 15 cm (6 in) of fill over the existing grade can cause the death of a mature evergreen.

- Support or remove damaged limbs and maintain root cover by adding soil or mulch when necessary. Attend to any damage. Damaged roots, trunks, and limbs can cause major trauma to a tree.

- Discuss with your contractor how to protect existing drainage patterns to maintain water flow to trees and shrubs.

Controlling erosion during construction

Bare soil is susceptible to erosion by water and wind. Erosion reduces your property's value by taking away rich topsoil, loading water bodies with damaging sediments (and possibly toxins), and damaging fish and wildlife habitat. A few basic principles will help you protect soil and water from potentially harmful construction practices.

- Make sure your contractor has a full copy of your building and lot protection plans for reference, to keep the disturbed area as small as possible.

- Fence off areas that are not to be disturbed.

- Avoid construction at very wet times.

- Consider working only in small areas and stabilizing each site with mulch or by reseeding before disturbing another.

- Insist on erosion control methods and equipment appropriate for the size of your project.

 **CAUTION**

Clear the minimum area required for your building and site access.

“ *My neighbour's contractor convinced him that clearing his entire site at once would save him a lot of money. Since then he has had major runoff problems and has had to dig drainage trenches all around his waterfront house.* ”

Shoreline resident

tip *During construction, block off the shoreline with a temporary construction fence to prevent damage by construction crews.*

Block access to your septic drainfield by construction vehicles, to prevent damage from anyone driving over it.

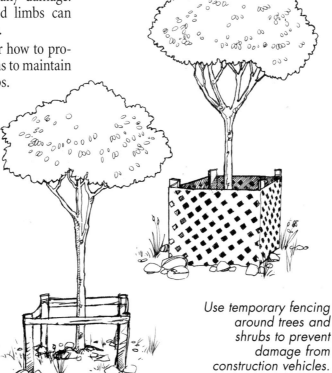

Use temporary fencing around trees and shrubs to prevent damage from construction vehicles.

Monitor your contractors!

Most contractors are specialists in their respective fields. Don't expect them to be experts in all things. For example:

- Your builder may specialize in energy conservation – but probably has not thought about details like keeping bugs out of your house.
- The plumber who installs your water softener may not know about what makes your septic tank work efficiently.
- The surveyors who you hire to find your boundaries are expert at finding survey pins – but they may slash a lot of vegetation (including healthy young trees) in the process of doing so.

We learned the hard way the importance of keeping an eye on sub-contractors when we left a trusted tree feller alone for too long and came back to discover that several trees had been cut down unnecessarily.

Sarah and Clive

tip *Be on-site to monitor your contractors whenever heavy equipment or tree felling is involved. A lot of damage can be done in a few minutes!*

Protect water quality

To protect water quality, you will need a two-fold strategy. First, keep clean water clean (i.e., by stopping it from running through your construction site) and second, keep any water that does become dirty from flowing downhill towards the nearest water body.

- Place silt fencing downhill of your building site. This fine material allows water to escape while catching soil particles.
- Use temporary straw bale diking uphill of your building site. Straw bales can be used to direct runoff while catching soil.
- Use only clean, debris-free fill that contains rock, sand or gravel.
- Cover fill piles (e.g., to be used for backfilling the basement foundation) with tarps. Uncovered fill will erode away, making a mess of your site and destroying wildlife habitat. Avoid extended use of plastic and tarps, however, as they also will cause increased runoff which can lead to erosion elsewhere.
- Check your site after major rainfalls and correct any erosion problems. If possible, go on site during a storm and observe what is happening to runoff.
- Make sure equipment is in good working order. Monitor it regularly to avoid leaks of fuel, oil, etc. which could contaminate surface water.

Protect bare ground

It is critical to protect exposed soil from wind, rain and other sources of soil erosion.

- Leave ground covered until it really must be uncovered.
- Promptly cover soil that has been exposed.
- Keep as much of the construction site covered at any one time as possible; minimize disturbance of ground cover like shrubs or grasses to avoid exposing soil and causing erosion or potential slope failure.
- Cover bare ground with mulch or burlap to limit erosion. Hold mulch down with nylon netting. If possible, mulch bare ground at the end of every day.
- Use a straw mulch to cover disturbed areas after reseeding. One bale will cover 45 sq m (500 sq ft).

Minimize the impact of machinery

Heavy machinery will compact soil and decrease its fertility, making it difficult to landscape your site after construction. Heavy equipment can also damage or kill trees and contribute to erosion problems.

- Use tracked vehicles whenever you can, especially in wet conditions. They exert less pressure on the ground than equivalent sized wheeled vehicles. For small jobs, consider hand labour for levelling your site or rent a miniature tracked excavator.
- Use the best machine for the job. "Skimping" will cost you more in the long run.
- Work in the driest part of the year to minimize soil damage.
- Devise a traffic flow strategy with your contractor in order to limit driving over the site. Restrict machinery and subcontractors' vehicles to established access routes.

Use safer construction materials

Choose the least toxic materials possible to minimize environmental risk both inside and outside your home.

- Use latex instead of oil-based paints.
- Avoid products held together with glues containing formaldehyde and other toxic chemicals. Look for particle board, fibreboard, plywood and blockboard which are marked "formaldehyde-free", or "low-emission".
- Minimize your use of pressure-treated lumber. If you do use it, wear a mask while sanding and sawing, catch all sawdust (with a tarp or plastic sheeting) and dispose of it in the garbage. Do not let sawdust fall on areas where it can get picked up by runoff and carried to surface water.
- Keep your site clean. Pieces of insulation, scraps of shingles, left-over drywall, and other materials are unsightly and may eventually pollute your land and water.

Dispose of construction debris appropriately

Construction waste is often toxic and must be disposed of properly.

- Never dump construction materials over the edge of bluffs or into ravines. Instead, make sure you have a waste container on hand from the beginning of your project that you can have hauled away at the end.
- Burn only waste construction materials which will not pollute. Chipboard products, treated lumber, plastics, solvents, oils, and asphalt shingles give off toxic fumes and leave a very toxic ash.
- Dispose of excess fill away from water, wells, wetlands, and trees.
- Have a plan for using any excess concrete (e.g., make a couple of forms in advance for concrete patio blocks). If necessary, use heavy duty plastic sheeting as a "drop area" for excess concrete. Never allow concrete wash water to run to surface water, or towards trees. The lime in concrete kills both fish and trees. Remove hardened concrete to reduce lime concentrations; then wash out concrete mixers far away from trees, and in an area where runoff will percolate through the soil and not enter water bodies.

Prevent spills!

Most construction projects require the use of materials dangerous to us and our environment. It is much easier to prevent spills than to clean up after they have happened.

- Do not keep excess amounts of harmful materials like petroleum products, cement, chemicals, soaps, or paints out in the open.
- Designate containers for specific uses with highly visible markings (e.g., "CEMENT ONLY").
- Ensure that any on-site fuel tanks are in good condition and properly closed with a lockable cap.

- Use drop cloths or tarps when handling materials like cement, paint and fuels.
- Practise good site clean-up habits; accidents and spills are much less likely if you have a clean, organized work site.

Be prepared for spill accidents

Unfortunately, despite our best intentions, spills sometimes do happen.

Cement

High concentrations of lime in cement will burn your skin and do the same to the soil and water.

- If cement is spilled, scoop up as much as possible and dilute the rest with water.

Fuels and solvents

These substances prevent animals from breathing and kill plants and soil. Eventually, they make their way into water sources underground and may find their way into our wells and homes.

- Always keep a "Green Bin" on hand to deal with fuel and solvent spills immediately. *See sidebar.*
- Treat spills with absorbents such as kitty litter or sawdust. Place as much affected soil as possible in a sealed container, and save it for waste collection.

Use a Green Bin to clean up spills of toxic materials like gasoline, solvents and paint.

Did you know . . . Any work that may affect fish habitat must be approved by **Fisheries and Oceans Canada** and by **Alberta Sustainable Resource Development**.

tip *Always have a Green Bin on hand to clean up spills when they happen. It should include rags, absorbent material like kitty litter or sawdust, paper towels, a trowel, empty plastic containers with lids, and crystals for hardening spilled paint (available at hardware stores).*

- Immediately report any spill that you cannot handle to the environmental emergency hotline and ask for instructions on how best to proceed. *See Appendix 1.*

Paint and drywall mud

Scoop spilled paint or drywall mud, and affected soil, into a sealed container. If paint has spilled and has contaminated surface water, call Alberta Environment for advice.

- If you are on a septic system, avoid washing latex paint into your system. Instead, use a paintbrush spinner and a five gallon bucket. Deposit the paint-laden water in a dry well located away from drainage channels and surface water. Watch your painting contractor very carefully.
- Dispose of solvents (like paint thinner) only at a hazardous substances depot.

Landscaping your site after construction

Because soil around a construction site is usually heavily impacted by machinery and excavation, you will need to take extra care to help your land recover.

- If you have been working on a project over the summer, make sure that the areas affected are seeded or landscaped with ground cover by early fall. This will minimize erosion by giving grass or other plants time to sprout and root before winter sets in.
- If you are considering planting grass seed, identify the area that you will *actively* use and limit your lawn to this amount. Keep your lawn close to your house, preferably on the side *away* from the water, and consider leaving the rest of your site in natural vegetation. This will reduce your overall maintenance time and costs!

Spend the time to prepare your soil properly prior to seeding with grass. Healthy soil will result in healthy grass which requires less maintenance time to keep it looking good. Healthy soil also absorbs water, and reduces runoff to adjacent water bodies. Choose the right grass or ground cover for your site and soils, to minimize requirements for water and fertilizers.

- Work in organic material (such as manure, leaf mulch or compost) to help aerate and loosen the soil.
- The topsoil you stockpiled during construction will now come in handy. Use it before importing soil from elsewhere.
- If you do purchase topsoil, beware of weed seeds that can be present. Methods for controlling imported weeds include tilling, and the planting of native grasses and wildflowers.
- Consider harnessing the power of your construction machinery to help create wildlife habitat. For example, moving boulders and rocks or strategic placement of logs may help create some wildlife habitat. This will help offset the impact of your construction. *See Chapter 11.*

There are many groundcover alternatives to turf grass; a grass seed mix containing a high percentage of clover stays green longer and requires no fertilizer since it "fixes" its own nitrogen. If you live in a drier climate, it makes sense to use a drought resistant grass species. Check with your local nursery for some good options.

- Plant alternatives to turf grass on erosion-prone slopes, on steep slopes, in shady areas, or in poor or compacted soil. Grass will not grow well in these areas.
- DO NOT extend your lawn to the edge of a steep slope; keep a wide strip of native vegetation to help protect the slope.
- Beware of "wildflower" mixes; they can include species of non-native plants, some of which might become aggressive invaders. *See Chapter 7.*

Resources

Caring For Shoreline Properties: Changing the Way We Look at Owning Lakefront Property in Alberta. 1999. Valastin, Pat. Alberta Conservation Association. Edmonton, Alberta.

Fish Habitat Conservation and Protection: What the Law Requires. Fisheries and Oceans Canada. www.dfo-mpo.gc.ca/habitat/ Law_Req/english/index_e.htm

Protecting Our Waters: Understanding Shoreland Best Management Practices. 1998. University of Minnesota Extension Services. www.shore-landmanagement.org/ depth/bmp.pdf

Working Around Water Fact Sheets. Fisheries and Oceans Canada. (204) 983-5163 www.dfo-mpo.gc.ca/regions/ CENTRAL/pub/fact-fait/fact-fait_e.htm

⑤ Septic Systems

Out of Sight, Out of Mind?

O ne septic system calamity is enough for anyone! After the incident when the system backed up during our party, I thought I'd be smart and bought bulk supplies of a septic enzyme additive. I used it regularly for several years, patting myself on the back for being so organized and responsible. So, it came as quite a shock when I learned that septic additives were not only unnecessary – but some may be harmful!

If you are not connected to a municipal or private sewage treatment system, you most likely have an on-site septic system to treat the sewage from your household. Even if you have an outhouse, a holding tank or a dry well – please read on! Much of this chapter is about septic tank and drain field (also known as leaching bed, disposal field or absorption field) systems, but the tips on maintenance are useful for most situations.

Even though it's out of sight, don't put your septic system out of mind! It is in your best interest to maintain your system properly, and avoid succumbing to myths as I did.

Maintaining a healthy septic system will help you:

- Save thousands of dollars in septic repairs or replacement.
- Prevent contamination of drinking water.
- Avoid potential health risks that can be related to failing septic systems.
- Protect water quality for swimming and boating.

Shoreline and streamside properties may pose extra challenges for septic systems. Wet soil conditions can make it more difficult for your system to treat wastewater effectively and sloping shorelines may allow harmful pollutants to get into the water body that you live beside. Because you live so close to water, it's even more important to take extra care of your system. It makes sense to dispose of your sewage effluent as far away from surface water as possible. This may mean pumping it uphill.

How Your Septic System Works

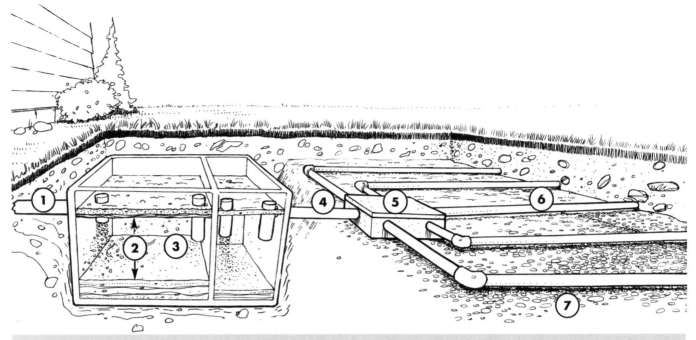

1. Liquid and solid wastes pass down the pipes and enter your septic tank.

2. The heavy and light solids separate. The heavy solids sink to the bottom of the tank as sludge and the lighter solids float to the top of the liquid forming a layer of scum. The layer of liquid in the middle is the effluent.

3. Friendly bacteria work to break down the scum and the sludge.

4. The effluent flows out of your septic tank when new wastewater flows in.

5. Effluent flows into the distribution box.

6. The liquid is sent out in various directions through a number of perforated pipes to the drain field.

7. Effluent seeps out of the holes in the pipes into the drain field. Some of it evaporates through the soil, but most of the liquid is absorbed through the gravel bed into the surrounding soil. Here, harmful bacteria, viruses, and other contaminants stick to soil particles and are broken down by a second batch of friendly bacteria.

A well-functioning septic system can work for many years and ensure that your health and that of nearby waterways is protected. It uses natural processes to treat the bacteria, viruses and other contaminants present in our wastewater.

> *When you live next to water, you can never flush and forget.*
>
> Ray Ford

In addition to bacteria and viruses, two components of sewage which are important for you as a waterfront resident to treat are phosphorus and nitrogen. Just a small amount of additional nutrients can make a big difference to water quality. In a well-functioning system, these elements are treated by the septic process, and absorbed by soil and plants. However, if your septic system is older, not up to standard, or not maintained properly, excessive quantities of phosphorus and nitrogen will pass through the soil and into surface water. The result can be algal blooms and overly abundant plant growth in the water.

Too many aquatic plants can make the water less enjoyable for swimming and boating, and the resulting depletion of oxygen can even kill fish. This is why it is important to leave as much space as possible between your drain field and the water, and to let your shoreline buffer fill with vegetation.

Maintain! Maintain! Maintain!

As many as one half of all septic system failures are a result of poor maintenance. Think of your septic system as a new car; regular maintenance helps protect your investment. Use these guidelines to help keep your system trouble-free.

1. Reduce water use

A healthy septic system functions best when you minimize water use in order to keep solid sludge well settled on the bottom of the tank. Excessive water flowing into the septic tank can cause the sludge to be disturbed and allow the solids to pass out of the tank where they can clog the distribution box, your drain field pipes and even your drain field.

When this happens, effluent cannot properly drain into the soil. Instead, it will be forced upwards without having gone through the second "friendly bacteria" soil treatment process, and untreated sewage may appear on the ground's surface. Or, your septic system could back up.

The best way to prevent these malfunctions is to conserve water. *See Chapter 10 for tips on how to do that.*

2. Pump out your tank

Pumping your tank on a regular basis is the most important step you can take to ensure the health of your family and protect water quality. If you have only a septic holding tank, you may need to pump as frequently as every week or two, depending on water usage and size of tank.

✔ Pump your tank every one to three years, unless you have a holding tank which requires regular pumping. Pump annually if your tank is undersized for your household, your water usage is high, or you have lots of guests.

✔ While your tank is being pumped, have your contractor check that the inflow and outlet pipes are free of blockages, and also check the condition of your distribution box.

✔ When pumping, make sure your contractor removes the sludge as well as the liquid.

✔ Keep a detailed record of repairs, pumping, inspections, permits issued, and other maintenance activities.

3. Avoid septic additives

Products marketed as septic tank "cleaners," "starters," or "enhancers" are unnecessary, expensive, and some can potentially shorten the life of your septic field. They do not replace the need for regular pumping.

In order to keep the effluent entering the drain field from your tank as clear as possible, you need to allow solids to remain intact, and accumulate on the bottom of your tank over time. Then have the tank pumped out regularly. This is the safest way to have your solid sewage removed. Additives might only break down the solids and send them into the drain field.

One myth about septic systems encourages people to put hamburger or a dead chicken into their system to increase the presence of bacteria. This only adds to the solid waste in your tank, and is completely unnecessary as your system creates more than enough beneficial bacteria on its own.

Frequent pumping is excellent insurance for all shoreline residents.

 CAUTION

If you do not maintain your septic system, you risk contaminating your water and affecting your family's health. Hepatitis, dysentery and other diseases can be spread by untreated sewage.

Did you know . . .

Many septic system failures are caused by overloading the system with too much water. A standard toilet sends 13-20 L (3-4.5 gal) of water per flush into your tank.

💧 ***Conserve water if you have a septic system. Purchase a low flush toilet, install a toilet tank volume reducer, or follow the old-fashioned advice of "yellow is mellow, brown goes down".***

> *We neglected to pump our tank for many years. One day, the system backed up when I did five loads of laundry. We had a major repair job to replace the septic field.*
>
> Shoreline resident

Did you know . . . Septic systems work best when the tank is warm (human body temperature). Consider warm washes in your laundry to help keep it that way.

tip *Download a poster version of our "septic tank with indigestion" and post it in your bathroom, to remind visitors to watch what goes down the drain! Visit our website for the free download:* **www.livingbywater.ca.**

4. Feed it a healthy diet

Septic systems thrive on human waste, but some things give them a stomach ache.

do

✔ Use basket strainers in all your sinks, tubs and showers to catch hair and food scraps. Hair is a big problem for septic systems and guaranteed to shorten the life of your field!

✔ Look for liquid detergents or concentrated detergents that don't have fillers and phosphates in them. *Check out Chapter 10 for ideas on alternatives.*

✔ Use a dry well (pits in the ground filled with drain rock) to backflush a water softener or a reverse osmosis unit, or to drain a hot tub, to lessen the load on your system.

✔ Use a lint filter on your washing machine; a stainless steel filter for the outflow hose is available.

✔ Install a passive effluent filter. Located at the outlet "T", it prevents suspended solids from leaving the tank. Effluent filters are inexpensive and reusable; however, they must be cleaned every six months and whenever the tank is pumped.

don't

✘ Flush facial tissue, paper towels, coffee grounds, tea leaves, fats or grease, cigarette butts, filters, sanitary napkins, newspaper, disposable diapers, condoms or metal. All of these items can clog your tank and field.

✘ Use a garburator. It adds solids which can fill up your tank and be flushed into your drain field.

✘ Use disinfectants which may kill beneficial bacteria in your tank, and minimize use of bleach. *Read Chapter 10 for alternative cleaners.*

never!

✖ Never use caustic toilet bowl cleaners and drain cleaners which can kill the beneficial bacteria in your tank. This results in sewage passing through without proper treatment.

✖ Never pour chemicals like paint, solvents, thinners, nail polish remover, kerosene, antifreeze, gas, or oil down drains; these are not broken down by the septic system and can seep into ground water, possibly poisoning your drinking supply.

Don't give your septic tank indigestion!

drain cleaners
hair
oil & latex paint, solvents
disinfectants or bleach
dental floss
facial tissue
paper towels
coffee grounds
grease
cigarette butts
sanitary napkins
disposable diapers
condoms
ground food from garburator
toilet bowl cleaners
antifreeze
oil or gas
flushable kitty litter
prescription drugs

5. Protect your drain field

● Don't drive or park vehicles on top of your drain field; they can crush your pipes and compact the soil.

● Don't allow large animals onto your field; over time, they can compact soil, as can extensive foot traffic.

● Don't drive snowmobiles across your drain field; they can compress the snow (your field's natural insulation)

● Do insulate your drain field, tank, and pipe connection against the cold. Undisturbed snow cover or straw are your best bets.

Evaluating Your Septic System

Finding your septic system

If you are new to a property, or have lost your records, you may not know where your septic tank and drain field lie. The regional Health Unit office or your local municipality may have a copy of the records, if the field was recently installed. Look for the **main sewer drain** and the **main pipe stack**. These will normally be on the same side of the house. Your septic tank will most likely be 1.5 to 3 m (5 to 10 ft) from the foundation, and will usually line up at right angles to the roof vent pipe. In winter, you may notice that snow melts more rapidly over the tank.

Now that you know where to look, start by using a metal rod to probe the ground carefully. If that doesn't work, try sending a metal plumber's snake down your sewer from the clean-out. When it meets resistance at the tank, go outside and sweep the area with a metal detector until you find the end of the snake against the tank. You may end up digging several holes until you find it! Then record the tank's location by measuring distances from three other fixed points (such as two corners of a building, and a tree). Use a 30 m (100 ft) tape to make this easier, and enlist a helper. Keep this record handy – post it in the basement or utility room.

Finding the distribution box and drain field may require some detective work. If you locate the drain field first, it will let you narrow down the search for the distribution box. Look for flat, grassed-over areas, and for tell-tale signs such as greener grass over the gravel trenches or, if there is only a shallow layer of soil over the gravel, drier grass. The trenches are generally 1.8 m (6 ft) apart, but may be 3.6 m (12 ft) in recent installations. In winter, you may notice accelerated snow melt over the drain field.

Once you have assessed the location of the drain field, you can estimate the likely angle for the sewer line from the tank to the distribution box. You may be able to find it by inserting a metal snake through the tank's outlet until it stops at the distribution box, and then using a metal detector to locate the snake. If all else fails, you can dig along your septic tank outlet line until it meets the distribution box. Use the same methods as with your septic tank to measure and record its location. Mark the location with one or two small concrete slabs, or a rock cairn.

Beware of old systems!

Some waterfront properties have older septic systems dating back to days when the property was used seasonally. These systems may lack adequate drain fields or have leaky tanks. Look for records such as the date when the system was installed or the date when the tank was last pumped. If no records exist, bring in a septic contractor to check your system and help you assess whether it complies with current standards and whether its condition is acceptable. You need to know:

- **Size of the tank** Is it large enough for your household? Does it have one or two compartments. Is there a second tank close to the first? *See Pg 39 for guidelines on sizing your tank.*

- **Tank condition** Is it structurally sound and leak-free? Are the inlet and outlet pipes and any inside tank features in good shape? Is the tank made of concrete, plastic or fibreglass? Does your tank have a wooden cover or an earth floor?

⚠ CAUTION

Warning signs that your septic system is failing:

- Grass over the drain field has patches which look abnormally healthy.
- There are soggy areas, areas with surfacing grey water, or areas with surfacing sewage on or near the drain field.
- Grass above the drain field is unusually wet.
- The sinks, showers and toilets drain more slowly.
- Sewage begins backing up in the toilet and drains.
- There is a sewage odour over the area of your drain field.

Did you know ...

Septic systems on older recreational waterside properties were not usually designed for heavy use and often have undersized tanks and drain fields.

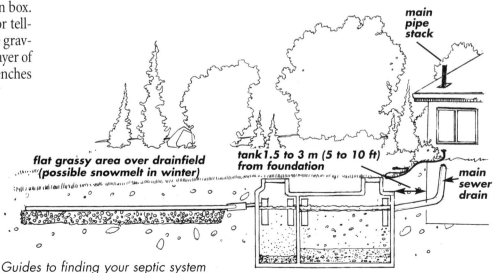

flat grassy area over drainfield (possible snowmelt in winter)

tank 1.5 to 3 m (5 to 10 ft) from foundation

main pipe stack

main sewer drain

Guides to finding your septic system

> ❝ *We bought a property next to a stream. The owners indicated an operating septic system. Once we'd moved in, we discovered that there was no drain field; instead, a pipe ran from the septic tank to the edge of the creek! We had to obtain a loan to have the system completely redone.* ❞
>
> Shoreline resident

- **Distribution box condition** How many outlet pipes are there to your drain field? Does the distribution box appear clogged or corroded? Is the box level?
- **Drain field specifications** What is the estimated total length of your drain field? Is there a drain field at all, or just a pit filled with rock (a dry well)?
- **Drain field setbacks** How close is the drain field to the water or to wells? *See Pg 37 for guidance on minimum setbacks.*

⚠️ **CAUTION: *Consider an immediate upgrade if you find any of the following features:***
- **Too small a tank.**
- **A tank with an earth floor.**
- **An inadequately-sized drain field or no drain field.**
- **A drain field that is too close to water or wells.**

You are risking your health and that of others. You may be able to obtain financial assistance (such as a low interest loan) from some lending institutions to help finance the upgrade.

Immediately report a septic system malfunction to your local Health Unit. Unpleasant as it may be, the alternative of not reporting your problem is potentially far worse. Your delay could cause widespread contamination of drinking water for many people, and you could be found liable for causing illness or death. Your local Environmental Health Officer will work with you to develop a plan to remedy the situation.

Repairs can range from clearing a few lines to replacing entire drain fields and removing contaminated soil. Depending on how long the problem has gone unnoticed and uncorrected, costs can range from a few hundred to thousands of dollars. Prevention of problems is the best alternative!

When You Buy Waterfront Property...

The rule of "Buyer Beware" holds as true for waterfront property as with any other purchase:

- If you are considering purchasing a developed waterfront lot, evaluate its sewage treatment system, and make any offer to purchase conditional on an inspection of the full system. Ask for copies of any approvals, and diagrams showing tank, distribution box locations and layout of the septic field.

  Remember: most home inspection services do not include the septic system in their inspection. You may need to organize a separate check by a septic contractor or independent consultant.

- An undeveloped lot, or one with only an outhouse, may not be suitable for a traditional septic system and you may be required to install an alternative system. If a subdivision was approved under old standards, some lots may be too small or may have unsuitable soil for a septic field system. Check with your local municipality to make sure the lot is big enough. There may also be a covenant against the property title affecting on-site sewage disposal or water supply. Check your title. If no "perc tests" (see Pg 38) have been carried out for the land you are thinking about purchasing, you may also want to include an acceptable perc test as one of the conditions of your purchase offer.

- In some locations, financial institutions require proof of an adequate and approved sewage treatment system before advancing mortgage loans.

Planning and Installing Your Septic System

Properly designed, installed and maintained, a septic system may last as long as 30 years. The savings and peace of mind obtained from a properly functioning system are well worth the expense of "doing it right" the first time around.

The application process

Before installing an on-site sewage disposal system, you or your contractor must apply to your local municipality for a development permit. Larger municipalities will also look after system approvals, soil classification or perc tests and inspections. Smaller municipalities will refer you to the Safety Services Branch of Alberta Municipal Affairs.

Evaluating your site

The most important step in designing a septic system is evaluating your property's soil and slope conditions, and determining an appropriate location for the tank and the drain field. Your septic system will need to be located in an area that meets three main requirements:

- **Soil suitability** The soil must not be too sandy, or too dense and clay-like. *See "Perc" test section on Pg 38.* Soils with too much clay do not allow liquids to be absorbed fast enough and soils with too much sand allow liquids to percolate too quickly, leaving the effluent untreated. There must be enough suitable soil (at least 1.2 m /4 ft) above the water table and above solid layers like bedrock or heavy clay.

- **Slope** Your drain field can be located only on ground with a less than 30% slope, where the trenches can parallel the slope contours.

- **Distance** Your septic field must meet minimum setback requirements. *See Resources.*

The rule with waterfront properties is "as far back from the water as possible." You want to leave as much soil as possible between your drain field and the water to absorb the nutrients and bacteria that will "leach" or seep from your septic field. In Ontario, engineers are finding that on some soils, setbacks of 300 m (1000 ft) may be required to adequately protect lakes from the seepage from septic fields!

If your property cannot meet these setbacks, you will need to explore alternative on-site treatment systems. You may need to consult an engineer or other specialist in waste treatment systems. *See "Alternative Systems", Pg 41.*

⚠️ **CAUTION**

Don't build, install, alter or repair a private sewage disposal system without first obtaining a permit from your local municipality. There are many eyes watching waterfront properties, and many complaints phoned in by neighbours.

Did you know . . .

The Safety Services Branch of Alberta Municipal Affairs and your municipality are not authorized to design your system, but must approve your design before installation can go ahead.

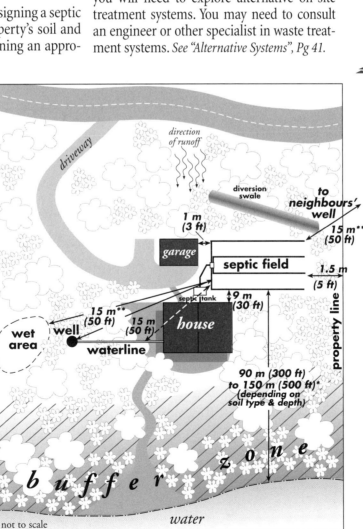

Minimum septic field setbacks

* Setback requirements can vary. The sensitivity of the shoreline, the presence of an environmental reserve and your building location relative to the septic field may also have some bearing. Check with your local municipality.

** The Alberta Standard of Practice requires a minimum distance of 15 m (50 ft) between a well and a septic field but for added safety we strongly recommend a 30 m (100 ft) setback.

" After our newly installed system had passed inspection, our contractor backfilled the site on a rainy day with a wheeled backhoe, damaging the drainage pipes in thirteen places. A tracked excavator would have been better in soft ground conditions. We had to hire another contractor to find and repair the damage. "

Sarah and Clive

 **CAUTION**

"Grey water" from hand basins, bathtubs, laundry and kitchen sinks must be treated by a septic system.

Placing a septic system

- Keep your septic system at least 3 m (10 ft) away from all trees and bushes, and at least 10 m (30 ft) from poplar and willow trees.
- Choose a site for your drain field away from areas that tend to be wet – either year-round, in the spring or after a rainfall. It will not work properly when the soil is too wet, and you risk contaminating ground and / or surface water.
- Identify a satisfactory site for a second drain field before installing your septic system, and protect the site from development. If in the future your field fails, you (or your children or the next owners) will have a fallback option.

Conducting a "Perc Test"

Guidelines for perc tests are available in the Alberta Private Sewage Systems Standard of Practice. *See Resources.* For the first part of the test you must dig (by hand or with a machine) at least two holes to a minimum depth of 1.2 m (4 ft) in order to determine the subsurface soil conditions. Be sure to cover and flag the observation holes and leave the excavated material undisturbed for the inspection.

To carry out the perc test, dig at least two holes 20 cm (8 in) in diameter and 90 cm (36 in) deep in the area of your potential site. Then fill each hole with water and time how quickly the water drains from the hole.

You will come up with a number that is the soil's percolation rate, a measure of its ability to filter effluent. In the ideal soil, effluent percolates quickly enough to prevent pooling, yet slowly enough to be effectively treated. The results of the perc test will determine the length of your drain field.

Include the results of the perc test with your permit application. The Development Officer may come to your property to inspect your observation and test holes and evaluate your soil.

Choosing a contractor

Choose a contractor who is aware of provincial regulations, is experienced in septic system installation, and is familiar with the requirements for proper siting and installation of septic fields. Your ideal contractor will be familiar with the information in this chapter. Consider hiring a contractor who uses tracked rather than wheeled equipment. *Review the tips in Chapter 4 for choosing a contractor.*

Selecting a septic tank
Type of material

If you are buying a new tank, the primary choice is between concrete (sturdy, but expensive to transport long distances because of its weight) and plastic (lighter weight but more expensive than concrete). Ask your supplier for a tank made of sulphate resistant concrete; this will resist corrosion (sometimes a problem in acidic soil).

A perc test shows how long it takes for your soil to absorb moisture.

Style

Two-chamber septic tanks are preferable; in some areas they are mandatory. These allow greater separation of solids and liquids, which means cleaner effluent with fewer particles to clog your drain field. This extends the life of your drain field.

If your local supplier does not have two chamber tanks, install two tanks to gain the superior treatment that two chambers offer. Connect the two tanks using flexible pipe material, as one tank may settle or float up more than the other.

Size

When it comes to septic tanks, bigger is usually better. Install a tank large enough for both present and future needs. The more waste and water that leave your house, the greater the tank's capacity must be. Take into account any plans to expand your household, build a new bathroom or bedroom, or purchase additional appliances that use water (washing machine, dishwasher, jacuzzi, etc.).

Septic tank capacities are sized to hold three days' worth of sewage flow, calculated on the basis that daily sewage flow per person is about 350 to 450 L (78 to 100 gal) per day. A household of four people would therefore require a 5400 L (1200 gal) tank minimum. However, in our water-consumptive lifestyles, many factors can result in a family's sewage flow exceeding the average.

Internal tank features

Several features can improve the septic tank's design, help ensure effective wastewater treatment and prolong the life of your system. These include barriers to your wastewater as it enters and exits the septic tank, encouraging solids to settle, and various kinds of filters that remove particles as they enter and exit the septic tank. Talk to the Safety Services Branch or your septic tank supplier for information on what is available in your area.

Planning your distribution system

Increasingly, sewage disposal systems for waterside properties are being designed to have effluent pumped uphill, away from surface water. If your drain field will be higher than your septic tank, you will need to install a pump chamber to the tank. Float switch controls activate the pump when the tank is almost full, and the effluent is then pumped to the distribution field. An alarm rings in the event of failure (for example, a malfunction of the pump or the electrical system). When this happens, you could have a sewage backup into your house if you flush toilets or drain baths.

Conventional drain fields require perforated plastic pipe to be laid on a bed of gravel. The pipes are covered with more gravel and a layer of landscape cloth (geotextile) to prevent backfilled soil from clogging the gravel.

Plastic distribution chambers are a type of drain pipe that requires no gravel and improves the overall function of the distribution field because the effluent is in greater contact with the soil. They are lightweight, easy to handle and are great for islands and places where aggregate is hard and/or expensive to come by.

Wherever it is located, the distribution box must be level for even distribution of the effluent in the drain field. An improperly levelled distribution box can cause uneven usage of your drain field trenches, which can shorten the life of the entire septic field. *See Pg 40 for tips on levelling a distribution box.*

The length of pipe that you need for your drain field is determined by the results of your perc and other soil tests. Generally, the slower the water is absorbed by the soil, the more pipe is required to disperse the effluent. Talk to the Safety Services Branch for details.

Neither our plumber nor house contractor told us that water softener backflush can overload a septic system and should be discharged to a separate dry well.

Shoreline resident

 **CAUTION**

Install as large a septic tank as possible.

Remember all those summer visitors – and how close you are to surface water! If large tanks are not available in your area, install a second tank. You will gain all the advantages of an extra chamber. We recommend that your total septic tank capacity be at least one size larger than what the Development Officer advises. Spend a little extra now, rather than a lot more in the future on repairs.

Plan your distribution system with double the space between the trenches. This will secure you the space for a second alternate field system in the future.

Did you know . . .

Once your sewage treatment system goes into the ground, you become an **"Onsite Water Pollution Prevention System Operator"** and are responsible for the ongoing health and maintenance of your system. This is a job to be taken seriously, considering the risk to your family's health and the health of your water if your system is neglected, and the risk to your pocketbook if it fails.

> **I learned after I bought my house that the toilet wasn't hooked up to a septic field system, as I had thought. It was connected to a holding tank which requires frequent pumping.**
>
> Shoreline resident

Minimizing damage from heavy equipment

Heavy equipment can accidentally do a lot of damage in a short period of time. Take the time to thoroughly brief the operator(s), to ensure heavy equipment does not compact soil or crush the perforated drain pipe. *See Chapter 4.*

Tracked vehicles are preferable to wheeled ones for septic field installation; the tracked machine's even weight distribution makes it less likely to break buried pipes while backfilling, cause distribution boxes to tilt out of level, or compact soil. Monitor your contractor rigorously.

- Have the contractor stockpile and cover your topsoil in a separate area for later use. This avoids having to truck in topsoil later when you want to plant cover over your new field. Importing topsoil is costly and brings with it the risk of importing weeds.
- Work with the contractor to minimize the risk of erosion and silt-laden runoff to the water from exposed soil. *See Chapter 4.*
- Locate a drop site for drain rock.
- If possible, install your septic system in summer or early fall when the ground is dry. It is harder for heavy equipment to work without damaging soil and vegetation when the ground is wet.

Septic system installation
do

✔ Ensure the base of the excavated area for the tank is level, free of rocks and has a minimum of 10 cm (4 in) compacted bedding sand. This prevents settling problems and/or fracture cracks in the concrete caused by the weight of the tank and its contents.

✔ Install flexible connectors between tank and outlet sewer lines. These protect your sewer line from breakage if your tank settles when full.

✔ Maintain or plant grass, trees, and shrubs downhill of your drain field.

✔ Invest in a "riser" for your tank. Essentially an access port, this inexpensive piece of equipment allows you to easily monitor your tank and prevent any problems before they happen.

✔ After installation, spread your topsoil over the new field and revegetate as soon as possible. Let grass grow at least 8 cm (3 in) high to promote better absorption of discharge.

✔ Direct roof, driveway, and other run-off away from your septic tank, distribution box, and drain field to avoid adding extra water to the soil. If necessary, contour the ground to create shallow ditches or swales.

✔ Spread extra soil over your drain field after a year or so if there is any settling of the backfill. This prevents stormwater and snowmelt from pooling over the drain field.

✔ Use heavy duty CSA approved sewer pipe if any part of your system runs under road crossings or parking areas.

✔ Mark locations of the tank and distribution box with stakes, concrete slabs, or rock cairns, and draw a sketch map of your system to make the parts easier to find in the future.

✔ One year after installation, open the distribution box and inspect for level by pouring in water and observing the flow of drainage. Plastic caps with off-centre holes, or "flow leveller", can be inserted into the outlet pipes to quickly adjust levels and compensate for an out-of-level distribution box. Also check for any corrosion of a concrete distribution box.

don't

✘ Plant trees or shrubs too close to your field or tank. Roots (especially those of willows and poplars) can cause damage and clog your drain field.

✘ Bury your drain field under landscaping materials (such as plastic) or pavement; water must evaporate from the drain field for it to work efficiently.

✘ Bury your septic tank under a driveway or deck, making it inaccessible for inspections and pumping.

Alternative Systems

Alternatives to the conventional septic system may be required if a property has insufficient setbacks from water, inadequate drain field area, or soil that doesn't meet percolation test standards. Approval from your municipality and/or the Department of Municipal Affairs is required for the design and installation of any alternative system. More research is being conducted all the time on these alternatives, so consult with engineers or contractors specializing in on-site sewage treatment systems. Your local Development Officer may also be able to provide suggestions for contractors in your area.

Alternative septic systems

A wide variety of alternatives to the traditional septic field system exist. Most are based on a septic tank with a specially designed and constructed soil absorption system. Many of these systems require pumps and electricity to distribute the effluent through the absorption field.

⚠ **CAUTION: For all alternative systems, as with traditional septic systems, maintenance is critical.**

- The mound system elevates your drain field using sand, gravel or peat to provide sufficient soil depth for treatment. A pump chamber is required to pump the effluent into the elevated area. Some systems use pressure "dosing" to ensure even distribution of effluent throughout the drain field.
  - Leave the mound undisturbed (even by children playing on it).
  - Plant short-rooted vegetation to cover the mound.
- A sand filter is a treatment bed used when there is limited soil, small lot sizes, or difficulty in meeting setback requirements. It introduces an intermediate treatment step, filtering the effluent through a bed of sand before it enters the drain field.

Aerobic treatment units

This system works much like a mini-municipal sewage treatment plant, where wastewater is mixed with air to promote faster and more complete treatment.

These units (also called package treatment units) are more expensive than conventional systems, as they require motor-run aeration devices and more frequent maintenance. They do provide a good alternative where soil conditions or setbacks are problematic.

Like septic systems, aerobic treatment units do not treat nutrients completely, so water discharged from these systems may have a high content of phosphorus and nitrogen.

- Discharge as far away from surface water as possible.

The composting toilet

Composting toilets, like septic tanks, use bacteria to digest human wastes in an environment with the right oxygen, moisture, heat and nutrient levels. A well maintained composting toilet can reduce waste volume substantially and uses very little or no water. They are usually emptied every 1-2 years, and produce well treated, odourless compost.

Composting toilets require careful maintenance, and may only be considered suitable in some circumstances.

Holding tanks

Holding tanks hold, but don't treat, wastewater.

⚠ **CAUTION: An older tank may have developed leaks, so check that it is watertight.** Holding tanks need to be pumped out frequently, and usually require an ongoing contract with a pumping service. They are an adequate long-term solution only if you are prepared to conserve water diligently, and pay the costs of frequent pumpout.

Older systems

If you have an outhouse, a dry well, or a below standard system – do everything you can to install one of the alternatives on this page, or a traditional system that meets today's standards. You'll rest more easily knowing you're helping protect water quality!

> *We thought we'd died and gone to heaven when we bought our waterfront home...until we started renovating! We had to install a package treatment plant and obtain approvals from all kinds of agencies. We're still waiting for one more approval.*
>
> Shoreline resident

Did you know ...

In some areas in Canada, lakeshore properties are only permitted septic holding tanks which must be pumped out frequently.

Resources

Alberta Private Sewage Systems Standard of Practice. 1999. Safety Codes Council.

Septic System Maintenance Pure & Simple: A Guide for Homeowners. Environment Canada and Central Fraser Valley Union Board of Health. www.hlth.gov.bc.ca/ protect/pdf/sep_english.pdf

Septic System Owner's Manual. 1999. Kahn, Lloyd et al. Shelter Publications. Bolinas, California.

6 Water, Water, Everywhere...

But is it Safe to Drink?

*F*ecal coliforms. The words made my heart sink. How could our brand new water system be contaminated? Our well contractor had taken a sample for testing a few days earlier when he was doing some work on the system. The lab report was clear: we had a problem. A second test gave the same result. We couldn't understand it, because previous tests had shown that the water in the well was fine. We bleached the whole system, and fortunately, that solved it. Later, in talking to our contractor, we discovered that just before he'd worked on our system, he had been doing some repairs at a neighbouring farm. We figure that he had inadvertently contaminated our water supply with his hands.*

Living on the shoreline gives you an intimate relationship with water. You see, hear and smell it every day – sunlight shimmering, the lap of waves, the gurgle of a creek. And you understand how crucial clean and clear water is to the health of all living things.

Canada has an abundant supply of water, and most of us think of good quality water as a basic right. Yet, increasingly we also face challenges with our water supply – both in terms of its quality, and in terms of availability. *For information on water conservation, refer to Chapter 10.*

Where Does *Your* Water Come From?

All the planet's water is part of the same interconnected "water cycle". Whether you draw from a well, use surface water, or collect rainwater and filter it, water is "recycled" over space and time.

Wells tap into **groundwater** – water below the soil surface which is stored in underground rock and soil formations called **aquifers**. **Surface water** refers to the water found flowing in streams and rivers, and stored in lakes, wetlands and the ocean.

Groundwater and surface water are linked. During times of heavy rainfall or snowmelt, groundwater is replenished by surface water. In times of drought, the water in the ground slowly discharges and helps keep streams flowing.

When we clear land and replace vegetation with turf grass or pavement, we reduce the ground's ability to absorb water. This causes greater stream flows in spring, and in the summer, streams that dry up more quickly. Over time, it may also cause aquifers to become depleted. Wells that draw on those aquifers may begin to run dry in the summer.

⚠️ **CAUTION:** *Whatever your water source, you cannot take for granted that your water is safe.*

Land use around you and upstream can affect your water quality – whether your water source is a well or surface water. Things to watch for include:

- Direct runoff of road salt and sand into water courses.
- Seepage from landfills and garbage dumps.
- Industrial leaks and spills.
- Improper or heavy use of fertilizers and pesticides.
- Sewage disposal systems, including septic systems, that are too close to your water source or poorly built or maintained.
- Extensive use of a watershed for raising animals and/or logging.
- Extensive use of a waterway by engine-powered boats.

Did you know...
Almost 80% of drinking water in Alberta comes from surface water! Only 20% of us depend on groundwater sources.

There is the same amount of water on earth today as there was a billion years ago. The water we use is continuously recycled in the environment.

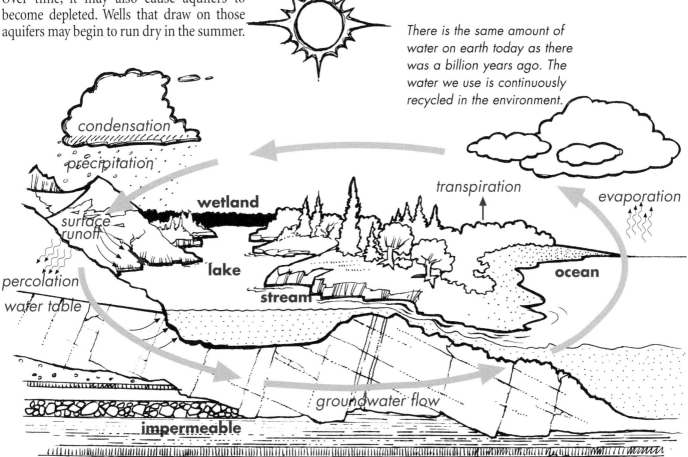

condensation
precipitation
wetland
transpiration
evaporation
surface runoff
lake
ocean
percolation
stream
water table
groundwater flow
impermeable

How Safe is Your Water?

tip **To learn more about collecting rainwater for irrigation, see Resources at end of chapter.**

tip **Protect your well water:**

1. *Ensure that your new well is cleaned and disinfected.* See Pg 47.

2. *Keep debris such as decaying vegetation or woodpiles away from the wellhead to avoid insect infestations.*

3. *Avoid using petroleum products or lawn chemicals near the well.*

4. *Protect the groundwater—do not flush hazardous liquids such as paint thinners, antifreeze, pesticides or motor oil down sinks or toilets.*

5. *Minimize use of water softener salt and caustic drain and toilet bowl cleaners—they pass through your septic system intact.*

6. *Protect any wetlands on your property.*

Surface water

If you draw surface water (from a lake, river or creek) for drinking, you are vulnerable to upstream pollution. As outlined in Chapter 3, buffer zones of vegetation are critical to protecting surface water from contaminants in runoff. Assess your own property and evaluate upstream or lakeside land uses to assess your risk.

If you are interested in helping test surface water as an indicator of the health of a water body, refer to Chapter 18 and Appendix 1.

Wells

If you draw groundwater from a well, regularly assess the well and surrounding area for risk of contamination. Wells on waterfront property tend to be shallow, since groundwater often lies close to the surface near lakes, rivers and streams. Shallow wells are generally more susceptible to local sources of contamination and to contamination by flooding. Some things to evaluate:

- Is your well on ground that's higher than the immediate surrounding area, to protect it from contaminated runoff from pets and livestock, or from flooding?
- Is there a buffer zone of vegetation or fencing to stop animals from going near it?
- Where is the well located with respect to nearby land uses that could contaminate groundwater? *See Pg 53.*
- Has the well been constructed properly? *Refer to Pg 51.* Is there any sign of deterioration?
- Are there any points of access for insects (shrubbery overgrowing the well, for example)?

⚠ **CAUTION:** *An abandoned well that is not properly filled, sealed, and capped provides a quick path for "unfiltered" water to damage groundwater quality, poses a safety hazard for small children and animals, and can affect groundwater reserves.*

Contact a reputable well driller to take an abandoned well out of service. The protection for you and your neighbours in the long run, from the costs of contaminated groundwater, will be worth the cost of the "decommissioning".

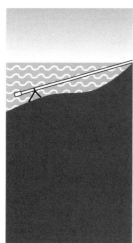

surface water

draws water directly from lakes, rivers, streams
- highest risk of contamination

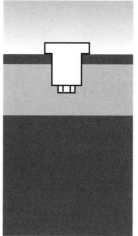

shallow well

draws groundwater from near the surface, can also take in surface water if near a water body
- high risk of contamination

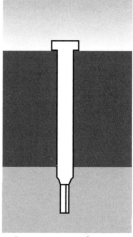

deep well

draws water from a protected aquifer, usually deep within the ground
- lower risk of contamination

Testing Your Water

Test your water regularly if you draw water from a well or surface water. Even if your water smells, tastes, and looks good, harmful substances may be present.

Sudden changes in appearance, taste or smell are a warning sign. Contact your local Environmental Health Officer (EHO) if you have concerns; he or she will work with you to determine if testing is advisable. Talking with your neighbours may also tip you off to potential problems.

Testing surface water

Alberta Health and Wellness does not make a standard practice of testing private surface water sources, even in areas where many people draw from the same source, unless there are concerns about contamination. The policy is that if your drinking water source is surface water, you are responsible for treating it to make sure it is safe from disease-causing organisms or other contaminants.

Water experts say that an untreated surface water source can't be considered bacteriologically safe for drinking, even if testing finds it free of coliform bacteria. Tests of untreated water are unreliable indicators of safety because surface water quality is quickly affected by factors such as runoff, or passing birds or boats, and the test only indicates water quality for the moment of sampling.

⚠️ **CAUTION: Test water drawn from lakes, rivers and streams after treatment.**

Testing well water

Test your well water at least annually for bacteria and any other chemicals which have been identified as a concern in your initial sample and whenever:

- A well is newly constructed or repaired.
- You begin using a well that has been out of service for a long time.

- There is a change in the taste, odour or colour of the water.
- A neighbour's well water is found unsafe.
- There is a chemical spill or accident nearby.
- Spring runoff might have made its way into your well or other nearby wells.
- Flooding has covered the wellhead.
- There has been a significant change in nearby land use.
- Family members or guests have recurrent stomach illness or diarrhoea (family members may reach a level of tolerance to contamination and may not show recurrent symptoms).
- A new baby is expected or an infant or expectant mother is coming on an extended visit.
- You open your cottage up in the spring (once you've given the water a few days to clear out the pipes).

It can be a challenge to assess your risk and determine how often to test your water.

💧 **tip** **Water sampling:**

1. *Prevent contamination by having clean hands and avoid touching the inside of the container or the cap. Watch where you put the cap down!*

2. *If you have an aerator on the faucet, remove it before taking the sample.*

3. *Wipe the end of the faucet, inside and out, with a bleach solution and run cold tap for at least a minute.*

4. *Take your sample early on a Monday or Tuesday; then ship it by overnight courier so that the lab can begin tests before the weekend.*

❝ *We just assumed that because everyone on our lake drinks the lake water, Alberta Health and Wellness must test it.* ❞

Shoreline resident

Did you know...

Foam and bubbles in lake or creek water are not always pollution. Sometimes when plant materials decay, fatty acids, similar to those found in common soap products, are formed, causing foam on the water.

If you suspect that a septic system may be contaminating your well, do a dye test. Your EHO can supply you with dye to flush down the toilet of the suspect system. If your tap water takes on the colour of the dye, you'll know the source of your problem.

Simple water testing kits that check for the presence of coliform bacteria are available at some hardware stores. If your water is usually good, you may want to use these as a less expensive check between lab tests.

The drinking water limits for some organic and inorganic chemical compounds can be very close to the lab's lowest detection limit. Make sure that you request testing using a method in which the lab's limit is much lower than the drinking water limit.

Finding a lab

Depending on your needs, the local health unit can test your water or you can use an independent lab. Look in the yellow pages, under "Laboratories – Analytical and Testing", or inquire at your local Health Unit. Choose a lab accredited by the Canadian Association for Environmental Analytical Laboratories. The lab will keep your records (we recommend you keep a copy as well). This way, you can track changes over time. Tests cost from $40 to over $200, depending on what you want to test for. When you contact the lab, they will send you appropriate containers and instructions for taking the samples.

What should you test for?

To meet Canadian Drinking Water Guidelines, municipal water supplies are tested for as many as 80 different parameters. It could be very expensive for you to test surface or well water frequently for this range of items; therefore most approaches to water quality suggest testing for **primary contaminants** – chemicals and organisms that may cause acute diseases or long term health effects, or which are likely in your area, either because they occur naturally, or are used in farming, business or households. Your local Health Unit can recommend which contaminants to test for.

Microorganisms

Of particular concern are **total coliforms** and **fecal coliforms** (*E. coli* is one type), *Giardia* and *Cryptosporidium*.

If your lab talks to you about "bacteriological testing", it will be for coliforms. They are used as indicators of contamination because they are easy to test for and not normally found in drinking water. Waterborne diseases such as cholera and dysentery are difficult to isolate from a water sample so if coliform bacteria can get into your well, it is likely that other disease-carrying organisms may also.

Some coliform bacteria grow and multiply in soils and decaying plant material, as well as in human and animal feces. While coliform bacteria are common on the ground and in surface water, they do not usually grow efficiently in well water.

Fecal coliforms are a sub-group of the coliform bacteria; most species, including *E. coli*, only grow in the intestines of warm-blooded animals. They indicate that your water source has been contaminated with fecal material. There are many strains of these bacteria, some of which are very harmful. They can cause nausea, diarrhoea and in rare cases, kidney failure and death.

Giardia and *Cryptosporidium* are intestinal parasites with a hard cyst form. They are difficult to kill with chlorine, but are fortunately very easily killed by boiling. These parasites are difficult to test for (labs that test for them are rare), and their absence in any one test doesn't mean that they won't be there in the future. They can inflict damage on the digestive tract, and are potentially fatal. Again, coliforms in the water sample indicate that there is a chance they may be present.

Nitrates and nitrites

These contaminants often enter our water sources due to improper use or overuse of fertilizers. They can cause oxygen deficiencies in the blood and can be very harmful to infants. Test at least once for nitrates and test again if someone in your household is pregnant or under eighteen months old.

Organic and inorganic chemical compounds

Chemical compounds with serious health effects include pesticides, solvents and PCBs. Heavy metals like lead and mercury can also contaminate drinking water. In some areas, compounds such as arsenic and fluoride are commonly found at levels above Canadian guidelines.

Secondary contaminants include naturally occurring minerals (such as iron, salt and calcium) or organisms (such as soil bacteria) that cause objectionable odours, tastes, stains, corrosion, etc. While they may be unpleasant, their presence in your water won't usually affect your health.

Interpreting test results

The lab will provide you with a written report of its analysis. Ask for a copy of the Canadian Drinking Water Guidelines so that you can interpret the results. Contamination of your water by nitrates or inorganic chemicals above allowable limits can have serious health implications and requires immediate action. However, if your results are slightly above the guidelines, contact your local EHO for information on how to proceed. The safety factors built into the guidelines may mean that your water is still fine to drink.

The most common serious type of contamination is bacteriological. There is no room for tolerance on the two measures of coliforms. They should read "0" and "0". The lab will advise you if your tests show that you have a serious immediate problem.

⚠️ **CAUTION:** *If fecal coliform bacteria are present, do not drink your water unless it has been boiled.*

Terms you might see on the lab report are:

Est. This means that the lab could only estimate total and fecal coliform bacteria, because a number of other bacteria grew in your sample.

O/G This means that the test sample became overgrown with other bacteria, so many that it was impossible to accurately determine if coliforms were present. These other bacteria may not be harmful, but they may mask the presence of coliforms because they grow faster.

< This means that if there are any bacteria or chemicals present in the sample, they are at a level lower than the lab could detect.

If the first sample shows the presence of coliforms, analyze a second to confirm the presence of any suspected contaminants. Stop using your water or ask your EHO for advice about boiling until you receive results from the second test. If your second test comes back still showing the presence of coliform bacteria, disinfect your system, then retest. If after disinfection you still have results showing coliform contamination, you will need to either identify the source of the contamination and eliminate it, or use a permanent treatment system.

Tracking sources of contamination

Contamination can enter a water system in a variety of ways.

- **During sampling** *See sidebar Pg 45.*
- **Problems with the well** It may lack casing, the casing may be punctured, the lid or cap may be ill-fitting or not in place, or surface water may be leaking in the top of the well or through poorly sealed joints.
- **Problems with the water source** Any source may be contaminated by nearby land uses or by an abandoned well that is not properly sealed. If you suspect that this is the case, consult with your EHO. Chances are that your neighbours will be experiencing problems as well.

Disinfecting your water system

Always disinfect whenever you construct or repair, or after a system has become contaminated.

- Pour bleach (5% chlorine) into your well in the quantity advised by your EHO.
- Start the water pump and open all taps. (If you have no pump, let solution stand.)
- Close the taps when you smell chlorine.
- Open the valve or plug at the top of the pressure tank before stopping the pump.
- Stop the pump.
- Close the valve or plug.
- Leave bleach solution in the water system for 24 hours.
- Start the pump, run water through the taps until the chlorine smell is gone. If a large quantity of chlorine has been used (for example, to disinfect a reservoir or cistern), dispose of the chlorinated water outside, far from the water's edge, rather than running it down a drain and into a septic system. Spray the disinfected water onto a grassy area, settling pool or dry well that will absorb and filter the water before it percolates back into surface or groundwater.
- Monitor your water quality and repeat as necessary.

Most labs offer package tests that test for a number of contaminants at one time. This is a cost-effective way to do a comprehensive test of a new well or when you purchase a property.

Test your own well water rather than relying on your neighbour's test to determine the quality of your drinking water. Wells only a few paces apart can have totally different water quality.

Treating Your Water

If your water is persistently contaminated, if you would like to soften it, or remove undesirable odours or tastes, you will need to treat it.

There are many water treatment systems currently on the market, ranging from chemical additions to filtration systems. Each system has its advantages and disadvantages; you will need to decide which treatment options are most important to you.

It pays to shop around. Ask two or three water treatment companies to review your lab analysis report and provide suggestions. Before investing the considerable funds that a water treatment system will require, do your research.

It is essential to match the treatment device that you buy with the type of water treatment you need. Treatment systems that have been certified by the National Sanitation Foundation (NSF) or US Environmental Protection Agency (EPA) have undergone rigorous testing and give you some assurance that the product will actually work. However, there are still many acceptable systems that may lack certification.

⚠️ **CAUTION:** *Whether or not your system meets these standards, it is a good idea to test your water routinely to ensure that your system is working properly.*

Types of water treatment

The most suitable types of water treatment for individual property owners are summarized below. Chlorination combined with filtration is one of the main treatment options recommended by Alberta Health and Wellness. For further information on many of these treatment options, consult with local contractors, your local EHO, or check Resources at the end of the chapter.

Check with the product manufacturer regarding the particular model you wish to purchase to ensure that it will give you the type of water treatment you need. You will need to weigh many factors, such as cost of the system, amount of treatment provided, convenience, maintenance requirements, and potential risks to health of **not** selecting a particular option.

These tables are not comprehensive, and consumers are responsible for checking the specifications on any products purchased.

Did you know ...

Banks and lending institutions are frequently asking for verification that your water system meets current standards, before advancing funds for mortgages.

---

tip **Buyer beware! Compare a number of different water treatment systems, check out the dealers' reputations and make sure you're not paying for a type of system that you don't need or want. We've heard of cases of unwary purchasers spending over $4000 on a system when a $2000 system would have worked as well or better.**

Chemical Addition

Chlorine (with carbon filter)		
Effective on:	bacteria; viruses; and if filter is so certified, lead and organic chemicals, some minerals
Ineffective on:	cysts (*Giardia* & *Cryptosporidium*); inorganic chemicals
Pros:	can provide treatment for the whole house
Cons:	can be expensive (drip or pellet chlorinators are least expensive; water needs to be filtered to prevent the formation of carcinogenic trihalomethanes
Softener Salt		
Effective on:	minerals like calcium and magnesium (hard water)
Ineffective on:	bacteria; viruses; cysts; organic and inorganic chemicals; heavy metals
Pros:	rids the water of metallic tastes, bad odours; avoids staining, scaling, and corrosion of appliances that use water; requires less detergent in the washing machine or dishwasher
Cons:	does not eliminate any contaminants that pose health risks; can lead to failure of septic field from overload of softener salt (potassium based salts are less harmful)

Filtration

Carbon block filter		
Effective on:	organic chemicals; minerals; taste and odour; and if certified to do so, cysts and lead	
Ineffective on:	bacteria; viruses	
Pros:	inexpensive; simple; good as a final filter, once water has been treated for microbes	
Cons:	bacteria may grow on filter if not well maintained	

Ceramic filter		
Effective on:	most bacteria; cysts	
Ineffective on:	chemicals; viruses; heavy metals; minerals	
Pros:	inexpensive; simple	
Cons:	fragile; must be carefully installed and maintained	

Iodinated resin (with carbon filter)		
Effective on:	bacteria; cysts; viruses; some organic chemicals; heavy metals	
Ineffective on:	inorganic chemicals (e.g., nitrates)	
Pros:	no electricity required; very small amounts of iodine required meaning very little enters our bodies and the environment	
Cons:	more expensive than ceramic/carbon filter; suspected of causing thyroid problems and affecting people prone to allergies	

Reverse osmosis (with carbon filter)		
Effective on:	organic and inorganic chemicals; heavy metals; cysts; fluoride; minerals	
Ineffective on:	bacteria; viruses	
Pros:	convenient	
Cons:	expensive; wastes water; can overload septic system with wastewater; requires consistent pressure of 240 to 275 kPa (35 to 40 psi); fragile	

Other

Boiling		
Effective on:	all microorganisms	
Ineffective on:	heavy metals; some organic chemicals	
Pros:	simple; effective	
Cons:	requires storage of treated water; time-consuming	

Distillation		
Effective on:	almost everything	
Ineffective on:	some volatile chemicals, except if paired with carbon filter	
Pros:	produces extremely clean water	
Cons:	slow, expensive; requires a lot of electricity and manual filling; water lacks minerals and may have unpleasant taste	

Ultraviolet radiation (UV)		
Effective on:	bacteria; viruses; some units work on *Giardia* and *Cryptosporidium*	
Ineffective on:	organic and inorganic chemicals; heavy metals	
Pros:	can provide whole house treatment; less expensive models are available for "under the sink"	
Cons:	water must be sediment-free; can be expensive to buy and maintain	

Test your well water during spring runoff as well as at the low-water time of year to get an idea of the potential variations in your water quality.

 CAUTION

Once you have a system installed, follow the recommended maintenance procedures. Depending on the nature of your water and your treatment system, maintenance may be required more frequently than the manufacturer's recommendation. Forget your system at your peril!

Buying Waterfront Property

Lawyers report that disagreements over water cause some of the most complex legal cases between neighbours. If you are considering buying land without an assured, and legal, source of potable water, do not assume that you will be able to make an "arrangement" with a neighbour.

Consider making your offer to purchase conditional on a comprehensive water quality test, drilling a satisfactory well, or proof of an existing approvals for a permanent water line. (This could be at the present owner's expense.) The lack of a good water supply can cause possible health problems, and seriously affect your property value when you wish to sell again.

Pass on your records of drinking water tests to new owners, should you sell. They'll thank you!

Plan for Visitors!
As a waterfront resident, you can expect lots of visitors! Make sure you have enough water for those busy summer weekends by installing a cistern or water reservoir. We've heard stories of unknowing visitors running wells dry from too many showers and loads of laundry.

Buying property which uses surface water

In Alberta, a water licence is not required to draw surface water for household use unless you use more than 1250 cubic metres (44,000 cu ft) of water per year. If you plan to construct a permanent water line, however, you may need a Licence of Occupation under the *Public Lands Act.* The term of this licence is twenty years and is renewable, but it does not automatically transfer upon sale of the land. If you are considering buying waterfront property which draws surface water, ask to see a copy of any licences. You may also want to contact Alberta Environment to confirm that the water intake system meets with their approval.

Buying property with a well

You will want to look first of all for any existing construction reports or well reports. They will tell you how and when the well was built. The well records may also tell you the water's rate of flow, essential to calculating whether there is enough water for your needs.

Talk to your future neighbours about their wells, and obtain advice from water supply professionals. These could include well drillers, or groundwater hydrologists or hydrogeologists. Also, ask questions of your Environmental Health Officer to identify any regional problems, e.g., arsenic or fluoride. And be sure to ask for results of any testing that has been done on water quality.

In order to avoid nasty surprises later, it can be a worthwhile investment to have a certified driller, well contractor or independent consultant inspect the well before you buy.

Assessing Your Well

Whether you are buying a property with a well, or wanting to take a good look at your existing system, here are some things to look for:

Well location

- Do nearby land uses which could damage water quality meet minimum setback standards? *See Pg 52 and Resources.*
- Is the well prone to flooding?

Construction

- How deep are the well and well casing? Shallow wells may be obtaining their water from surface water.
- How old is the well?

⚠️ **CAUTION:** *Older wells (more than 50 years old) run a greater risk of being contaminated.* They are likely to be shallow, and may have been poorly constructed with inadequately thin or corroded casings. Older well pumps might leak lubricating oils into the water. If you don't know how old a well is, assume it needs an inspection.

- What type and capacity of water pump (submersible or shallow) and pressure tank (buried, in basement or in pumphouse) are installed?
- Is there a supplementary storage cistern or water tank? What condition is it in?
- Check that the well is properly sealed with a modern gasketed well cap that extends 45 cm (18 in) above the ground.
- Does the well record show a sanitary grout seal and a well screen (for sand and gravel wells)? (Check with Alberta Environment or the owner for well records.)
- Is there a pumphouse, and can it be locked to prevent vandals from tampering with your well? Is the pumphouse clean and tidy? Ensure there are no solvents, fertilizers or other chemicals stored inside.

Water characteristics

- What is the rate of flow? How was it determined? Make sure the well can deliver what you and your visitors will require. In many jurisdictions the basic minimum is 6.75 L (1.5 gal) per minute.
- How long can the rate of flow be sustained? Check well records to determine if "drawdown" data (for well capacity) are available.
- What are the characteristics of the well water? If there are no recent lab reports available, have a lab carry out a comprehensive analysis of your water to determine if it is fit to drink.

💧 *You can get clues to water quality by checking your bathroom and kitchen fixtures.*

- *Toilets and sinks will have rust stains if there is an iron or manganese problem.*
- *Toilet tanks will have a slimy coating if there are iron bacteria in the water.*
- *Shower heads and faucets will have lime deposits if the water is hard.*

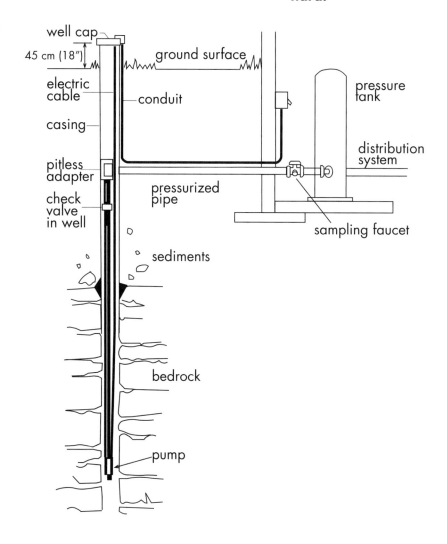

Installing Water Systems

CAUTION

Protect your water quality by following these minimum setbacks when installing a well.

tip *Guard against well and system contamination from backflow in your water supply line.*

- *Avoid submerging the garden hose used to fill a pool or hot tub; water can drain back into the well and contaminate it.*

- *Install a backflow prevention device (a check valve or vacuum breaker) on the water supply line.*

Wells

You can drill or excavate a water well in Alberta for household use without a licence. Searching for water, however, is still part art, part science. You can look at the database of well records (Alberta Environment), and consult with hydrogeologists. In many areas, aquifer maps are available; check with your local municipality or Alberta Environment.

Consider talking to neighbours before constructing your new well. Wells are expensive to install and it is impossible for a contractor to guarantee their success. Your neighbours' experiences could help you to make a wise decision about where to site your well.

Your neighbours may also be able to recommend a contractor. Be cautious about hiring someone just because they have the lowest bid. It may be more costly in the long run if they cut corners on construction to save money, so specify that proper well construction guidelines are used. Before hiring a driller, talk to two or three and select a certified contractor that has an approach that makes sense to you. *See Chapter 4.* Ask questions so that you both have an idea of what to expect, and how to proceed if problems arise:

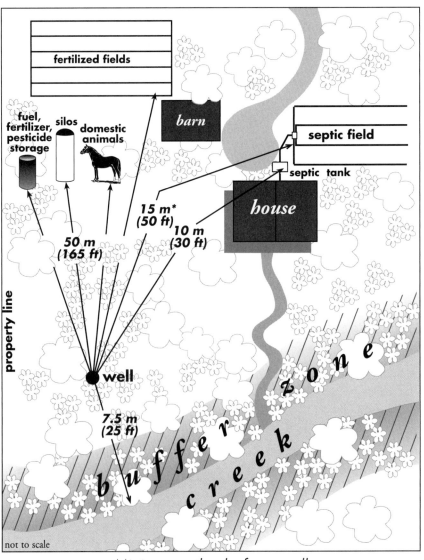

Minimum setbacks for a well

- Are you a certified contractor? May I see proof? How long have you been drilling wells in Alberta? Do you drill wells that meet provincial guidelines?
- How deep do you think we need to drill? How did you determine this?
- What quantity of water flow are you expecting?
- What is the geology like locally? Are you expecting to find water in sand and gravel or in bedrock? (The occurrence and flow of groundwater in bedrock is less predictable.)
- What are the chances of encountering flowing artesian conditions (where water is forced upwards under pressure) in this area? If we do, what will you do about controlling the flow? How will that affect my budget?
- What if we don't find water with enough flow? What will you suggest? (If drilling in rock you may be able to hydrofracture the well.) How will this affect my budget?

Remember to budget for contingencies. Results are always uncertain when drilling a well, so it's best to be prepared.

Siting and designing your well

- Make sure that you meet minimum setback criteria from sewage disposal and other land uses. *See diagram on Pg 52.*
- Locate the well so that the well head is easily accessible and safe to work at.
- Make sure the system design includes a sampling faucet between your well and your house. This will allow easy access to your untreated water for sampling purposes.
- Check that the system is designed to prevent backflow. When the system loses pressure, the normal flow of water is reversed, causing water in the system to drain back into the reservoir or well.

Surface water

If you obtain your water from a surface water source such as a pond, lake, stream, river or dugout, make sure that you disinfect and treat your water.

- To minimize damage through the buffer zone, use a mini trenching machine attached to a narrow excavator or bobcat when laying a permanent water line (don't forget the approvals). In ideal circumstances, the line will be at adequate frost depth, in the same "service corridor" as your shoreline access trail.
- Put your intake in a water body that is:
  - clean and preferably has a healthy, natural and stable shoreline.
  - free of sewage disposal systems.
  - protected from erosion.
  - protected from livestock area drainage.
- Locate a floating intake so that it draws the best quality water (deep enough, but above the bottom).
- Locate intakes upstream from sewer outlets or other sources of contamination.
- Don't drink surface water if you suspect a blue-green algal bloom. *For more information on blue-green algae, see Chapter 12.*
- Screen the intake with metal mesh, to keep out leaves, twigs, and other solids. Check regularly to make sure that the mesh is not clogged. If your intake is on a fish-bearing stream your mesh will have to meet Fisheries and Oceans Canada regulations.
- Use a submerged marker that won't interfere with boats or attract birds.
- Filter through an activated carbon filter.
- Consider using a settling basin to clear the water before filtering.
- Use gravel strainers with 50% sand to filter the water.
- Pump the water into a cistern or storage tank, especially if the water is subject to silt in the spring.
- Be wary when the water level is low. The water temperature is higher and its quality may therefore be poor.

> ❝ *We hired a local well driller from the phone book without talking to our neighbours. We should have realized something was wrong when he didn't do any site assessment before starting to drill. He just kept on drilling until we stopped him at 440 ft. At $20 a foot, that well cost us over $8,000 and only yielded 1/8 gallon a minute.* ❞
>
> Clive and Sarah

Resources

Cottage Water Systems. 1993 and 1999. Burns, Max. Cottage Life Books. Toronto, Ontario.

Planning Your Water System. Alberta Agriculture, Food and Rural Development. www.agric.gov.ab.ca/water/wells/module2.pdf

Alberta Environment Website on Water. www.gov.ab.ca/env/water.html

National Sanitation Foundation. www.nsf.org

Alberta Private Sewage Systems Standard of Practice. 1999. Safety Codes Council.

See Appendix 1 for complete Resources.

7 Shoreline Landscaping

or, What to do With the Urge to "Putter"

*I*t took a shoreline "mowing battle" to help me realize that I – who loved the lake – was hardly its friend. I had grown up believing in neat and tidy yards. Because I was running a resort, I thought that lawn maintenance was even more important. After all, I didn't want our guests thinking that a messy yard meant messy cottages! Clive, on the other hand, wanted the natural look. We had many "discussions" about the grass that had been planted years earlier along the water's edge. I was won over, however, when I learned that tall grasses, shrubs and trees along a shoreline help keep it healthy, and that a healthy shoreline is important for water quality and wildlife. So, we left the shoreline alone, and mowed less and less each year.

Whether it's mowing the grass, weed trimming, or landscaping a flower garden, many of us enjoy having outside projects to occupy our lives – sometimes even when we're on vacation!

In this chapter, we have identified eight activities for you to choose from, when the urge to putter or work around your shoreline strikes you. These eight projects may also help you make your shoreline healthier, help to protect your property from erosion and improve the ability of your buffer to protect water quality. **Of course, if your shoreline is totally natural, the best thing you can do is leave it alone!**

1. Rethink your lawn.
2. Thicken your shoreline buffer.
3. Prune trees to open views (rather than remove them).
4. Care for shrubs and trees once they're in the ground.
5. Deal with alien invaders.
6. Create wildlife habitat.
7. Soften a retaining wall.
8. Clean up garbage, leave natural debris.

 Read this chapter even if you hire others to do your yard work for you, to let them know what they can do differently to help protect your investment.

1. Rethink Your Lawn

Evaluate the areas on your property devoted to turf grass (lawns). How much of your lawn area is located within the "buffer zone"?

Alternatives to turf grass in "buffer" areas

In areas close to water or to the edges of bluffs, ravines, and banks, turf grass is a poor choice of groundcover. Its short roots mean that it is poor at binding soil, and this can result in erosion and land slumping. We tend to water turf grass, and this can lead to oversaturation of soil and slumping. Compared with native vegetation, turf grass also permits much more runoff (and pollutants) to pass over it towards surface water.

Because there are so many other plants that grow naturally along shorelines or streamsides, lawns located near water often require even more work than normal. We can spend lots of time and money weeding and mowing.

If you have turf grass in your buffer area, we recommend that you consider alternatives that will start to restore your buffer.

Enhance your buffer strip

By enhancing your buffer strip, you will improve its ability to protect your property from erosion and to filter pollutants from surface water. You will also reduce your lawn's size – and treat yourself to some newly earned free time by jumping off the lawn-care treadmill!

The easiest way to start a "buffer improvement program" is to leave a few metres of lawn unmown by the water's edge. Mother Nature will do a lot of the work for you!

- Mark off your buffer strip with ribbon or stakes to remind you to keep the mower out. Keep the edge "ragged" for a more natural look and to improve wildlife habitat.

- As new plants appear, let them grow, unless you know they are invasive. *See Pg 61.* In the first year, your grass will get taller and you may see wildflowers. Uncut grass grows longer roots, helping to hold your shoreline together. By about the third year, you'll see shrubs starting to move in. Sit back and enjoy your natural, low-maintenance shoreline protection!

- Consider increasing your buffer's width a little bit more each year. Ideally, a buffer needs to be at least 30 m (100 ft) wide to adequately protect water quality and provide a variety of native trees, shrubs and grasses for fish and wildlife habitat. Whatever you do will be helpful, however. Even if your property has development inside the buffer area, every little bit of buffer that you leave or create counts!

tip *Cover lawn areas you want to get rid of with black plastic or pieces of old carpeting, anchored with rocks. Leave in place for a whole growing season to kill the turf without the work of digging it up. Remove the covering and plant, or allow nearby native vegetation to gradually creep in.*

Keep your lawn as small, and as far from the water, as possible. Reduce maintenance by planting the rest of the area with native ground covers.

Did you know …

If you have an undisturbed, natural shoreline, the best thing is to leave most of it alone.

CAUTION

Keep all chemical fertilizers and pesticides out of the buffer zone – 30 m (100 ft) from the high water mark.

" I like to think I'm making a new fashion statement. It used to be that "tidy" was "in" for shorelines. Now, "tidy" is out, and "wild" and "natural" are in! "

Shoreline resident

Did you know . . .

"Clean" and tidy lawns make dirty lakes and streams! They can speed up runoff of dirty water, contribute to soil erosion and add a chemical load from the fertilizers and pesticides used on them.

tip *If Canada geese find your grass attractive, try reducing your lawn size and blocking access points with shrubbery and thick vegetation.*

If your shoreline area has been heavily cleared, you can help speed up the process of creating a buffer through planting. *See Pg 57.*

Practise good lawn care

In those areas of your lawn which are "upland" and outside of your buffer (as well as any lawn areas which are inside your buffer zone), practise special maintenance procedures to keep both your grass and shoreline healthier.

Weed seeds will not usually germinate in the shade of vigorous grass growth. If you live in an area which is dry in summer, plant a seed mix containing hardy drought-tolerant grasses or native perennials suitable for groundcover.

Mowing
- "Grasscycle": Use a mulching mower and leave grass clippings on your lawn. They will be gone in a few days and can increase your soil's fertility by up to fifty percent!
- For small areas, consider using a push mower – you will reduce emissions and noise pollution for your neighbours.
- Mow when the grass is as dry as possible to prevent clumping.
- "Mow it high and let it lie." Leave your grass at least 8 cm (3 in) long; this helps keep weeds from seeding, retains moisture in your grass, and encourages root growth.
- Keep mower blades sharp to avoid tearing the grass; this can result in increased water loss and susceptibility to disease.

Fertilizing
Chemical fertilizers are easily dissolved into runoff and carried into your water body. Their high concentrations of nitrogen and phosphorous can cause problems such as the overgrowth of algae.

CAUTION: *Consider all your options before bringing out the fertilizer spreader:*
- Plant alternative groundcovers that do not need fertilizer.
- Aerate your lawn to improve its health.
- Take a sample of your soil to a nursery or agricultural field office for analysis. They will determine what nutrients are lacking, and recommend fertilizer application rates.

- As a last resort, choose fertilizers high in Water Insoluble Nitrogen (WIN). WIN is released slowly and helps prevent "lawn burn" and groundwater contamination. WIN fertilizers cost more, but they're worth it. Avoid fertilizers high in phosphorous as they promote the growth of algae in your water body.

Weeding
- Be tolerant of "weeds"! Many have wildlife value, help build your soil, and keep your lawn green during dry times.
- Remove unwanted plants from your lawn using long-handled tools. Invest in a good quality weed remover and work when the ground is damp to make your job easier.
- Pour boiling water over the exposed roots of plants like thistle and dandelion. *See Pg 61.*
- If you feel you must use a pesticide, use an applicator which allows you to direct a small spray towards each unwanted plant. Avoid applying pesticides to your whole lawn and stay away from products like the fertilizer/herbicide mixes which provide blanket applications. *See Chapter 10 for more information on use of pesticides.*

Watering
- Hold water back in the spring to encourage root growth for sturdier, more drought-tolerant plants.
- To reduce waste and evaporation, use a water sprinkler that delivers large flat droplets and has an adjustable range.
- Encourage deep rooting by watering infrequently yet thoroughly. Depending on your local weather patterns, water your lawn so that it gets a thorough soaking of 2-3 cm (1 in) of water, every five to seven days. Water in the early morning, and avoid overwatering.
- In hot, dry weather, and during water shortages, allow lawn grasses to go into a state of dormancy. Water 7-12 mm (1/4 - 1/2 in) every two or three weeks to keep crowns from dehydrating beyond the point of recovery. The grass will look brown, but it will be dormant – not dead!

2. Thicken Your Shoreline Buffer

Speeding up the development of your buffer by planting will help you reap the benefits sooner.

A little bit of planning...

- Look at the site conditions on your property – aspect (which direction it faces), soil type, light, drainage, moisture, and degree of slope. These will all influence your planning, and help you choose suitable plants. Prepare a sketch showing your shoreline and features such as existing vegetation, buildings and driveway.
- Identify what areas you need for recreation. Are there other ways of meeting your recreational needs with less use of the shoreline? *See Chapters 9 and 14.*
- Identify those areas of your shoreline that you feel comfortable in letting revert to nature. Even if it's only a small area, it's a good start!

- Think layers for your shoreline. Incorporate low-lying ground covers, tall native grasses and wildflowers, shrubs, small trees and vines and, finally, trees that will grow tall with maturity. This way, you will create a more stable and interesting landscape, and the variety of plantings will help hold your shoreline together, and attract songbirds and other wildlife.
- To plant in an established lawn, remove just enough turf to plant your shrubs and trees, or remove larger sections and seed or replant with a variety of native grasses, perennials, shrubs, and trees.

Did you know ...
A natural shoreline is a haven for all wildlife, including birds and insects that prey on mosquitoes!

The Beauty of the Buffer

The key element in integrating shoreline protection with landscaping is protecting and enhancing your buffer zone – both the portion upland of the high water mark, and the portion that is aquatic.

If your shoreline still has abundant native vegetation, consider yourself lucky. Protect your shoreline and let it be. You have been blessed with a time- and money-saving gift from nature! This includes aquatic vegetation and shoreline areas below the high water mark.

Native plants – such as shrub willows beside a stream or poplar beside a lake – are already adapted to the growing conditions of your region. They are generally more resistant to disease and stresses than introduced plants and will save you from mowing and having to apply fertilizer, pesticides, and extra water. They also help protect your shoreline from erosion and provide natural habitat for wildlife.

The greater the variety of native trees, shrubs, perennials and grasses you have, the better for maintaining a healthy shoreline. And, *"the bigger the buffer, the bigger the benefits"*. Remember, at least 30 m (100 ft) from the high water mark is a good target to aim for to adequately protect water quality and wildlife habitat!

Ridges and berms are other elements of nature's buffer systems. Earth and sand ridges along lakeshores are caused by ice expanding and pushing against the shoreline. These natural formations help protect shorelines from erosion, and help filter runoff before it enters the water. Native vegetation will easily revegetate any buckled earth or sand dune formations. Resist the temptation to bring in equipment to level and grade your shoreline; keep berms and dunes in place on your property, and avoid cutting through banks to get to the water.

The benefits of restoring a natural buffer are illustrated in the colour insert included with this book.

tip *To help visualize what your shoreline will look like when it is planted, take photos of your shoreline from your deck or windows. Make colour photocopies and sketch possible locations for shrubs and trees. Create several alternatives to help you choose a planting pattern that frames the views you like most.*

What plants are "native" here?

To determine what would have grown on your property before it was cleared and altered, you may need to do some research.

- Look at nearby undisturbed shorelines. What plants exist there? If there have been many changes on neighbouring properties, look farther afield for examples. Local naturalist clubs or horticultural societies may have members who can help you.

- Compare your property's site conditions with those of nearby shorelines. If your site is open and exposed to sun, and other nearby sites have shade tolerant trees and shrubs, you may have to plant different species initially. Your job will be to imitate nature's changes over time, by starting with sun tolerant species, and then in a few years, when they grow and provide cover, planting more shade tolerant ones.

- Look at how the native plants are growing in relation to one another. Nature often puts plants in clusters, or "companion" plants two or three types together.

- Contact your local nursery for suggestions. Most nurseries stock native plants or can direct you to someone who can help. Check our web site for lists of native plant nurseries and resources.

 For detailed information on planting, see Chapter 8.

Aquatic vegetation

Be careful that your landscaping projects don't damage the area below the high water mark, including vegetation growing in the water. Leave water plants in the water!

Many of us call these water plants "weeds" – but, with the exception of some alien invaders, they are far from useless! They stabilize soil, trap sediments, and protect your shoreline from erosion. They also help keep water clean by absorbing nutrients and toxins, supply oxygen, and provide nesting sites for birds, habitat for fish and food for wildlife.

⚠ **CAUTION:** *In addition to being illegal, pulling aquatic vegetation can backfire!*

Removing plants from the water disturbs underwater sediment and can allow unwanted species like Eurasian milfoil to move in. Your water may become cloudy as sediment is churned up by waves, fishing may deteriorate as spawning areas are covered, or your shoreline could erode with the loss of its protective buffer.

- To restore native aquatic vegetation, or for advice on dealing with invasive aquatic plants, consult with Fisheries and Oceans Canada (DFO) or Alberta Environment.

- If you feel that aquatic plants have overrun your lake, consult with biologists at Alberta Environment. On some sensitive lakes, the extra runoff from human development has stimulated excessive aquatic plant growth.

A plan for shoreline restoration:

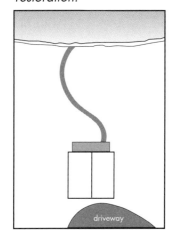

Year 1

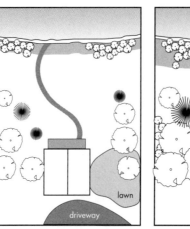

Year 2
Grass left unmowed along water's edge. Native shrubs and trees planted.

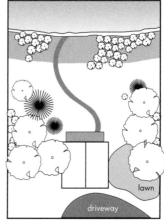

Year 4
Unmowed area is larger. More shrubs and trees planted.

Year 6
Healthy buffer zone, trees provide shade and wind protection.

3. Prune Trees to Open Views

Mature trees help maintain your property and increase its value. They help reduce runoff by breaking the eroding force of rainfall. They shade the ground, helping to retain moisture, and they shade the water, keeping it cool and providing habitat for fish and other wildlife. Trees along bluff crests and shoreline edges stabilize the soil. They also provide you with privacy, shade and wind protection.

Trees can be removed in minutes, but often require a lifetime to replace. Before you cut

trees down to get your perfect view of the water, think about the benefits they provide. With creative pruning and limbing (or windowing), you'll be able to obtain good views of the water, through trees and over the top of shrubs. Create your "view corridors" by identifying the branches that obstruct the view from your favourite locations in and around

your house and removing them. Through careful pruning, houses built on bluffs can have good views, even with tall trees growing below.

- Prune in late winter or early spring.
- If you're in any doubt, hire a tree specialist to prune properly and protect your investment. Improper pruning can weaken trees.

⚠️ **CAUTION**

Avoid topping trees; this can result in unsafe top-heavy growth, or encourage rot to set in through the cut at the top. Overly extensive pruning (over 25% of the crown) can kill trees and damage fish habitat.

Pruning conifers

windowing

interlimbing

skirting up

Pruning deciduous trees

before

after

incorrect

❝ *When we moved into our house, I thought the spruce trees would have to come down – it seemed so dark. But after a year, I had grown to love those trees and all the birds in them and couldn't imagine the house without them.* ❞

Shoreline resident

4. Care for Shrubs and Trees

Protect young plants from voles and mice with wire or plastic tubes.

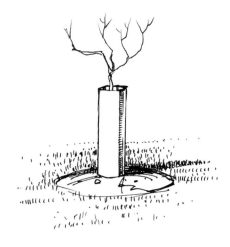

tip *If you want a tidy look to your shore-line landscaping, select native shrubs that have landscaping appeal such as red osier dog-wood, various shrub wil-lows and snowberry.* See Appendix 2.

Caring for shrubs and trees that you've planted will help ensure their survival, and protect your investment.

Protect young plants from wildlife

Several techniques can reduce or prevent wildlife damage to new plants. These will work best if carried out from the start.

- Keep rodents away by trimming grass and weeds within a 50 cm (20 in) radius of a new plant. Take care to avoid damaging bark with grass trimmers and lawn mowers.
- Protect stems of young plants with a wrap-around plastic spiral, agricultural drain, wire mesh, or plastic tree shelter.
- Individual fencing may be the answer for challenging wildlife, such as beaver or deer. With the tree or shrub planted, dig a circular trench at least 50 cm (20 in) away from the plant's base. Place wire fencing in the trench around the plant and stake it securely. If the plant is taller than your wire, place the fence even farther away from the stem so that the branches, and especially the plant tip are beyond nibbling reach. For more security from burrowing wildlife place a band of aluminum in the bottom of the trench.
- If you've planted a large number of trees or shrubs in one area, you may save yourself some time by fencing off the entire area. The height of your fence and mesh size of the wire will depend on the type of wildlife you are expecting!
- Provide decoy plants – something that is edible, and easier for the wildlife to get at than the one(s) you are trying to protect.

Provide follow-up care

Provide care to young plants for at least three years after planting. Even native plants can be overrun by competitors in the race for nutrients or water.

- Stake young trees and shrubs, or flag with surveyor's tape. This will help you find them if surrounding grass grows tall and threatens to choke them out. It will also make them visible and prevent them from being accidentally knocked or hit, especially when they are buried by snow.
- Mulch your plantings. If they are close to shore, watch for high water which can carry your mulch away. Choose from a variety of options:
  - Landscape or geotextile fabric. Avoid using plastic mulch to suppress weeds, particularly on slopes. It can alter runoff patterns and lead to erosion.
  - Thick layers of organic materials such as grass clippings, sawdust, leaves or straw. You can put the organic mulch on top of a layer of cardboard or newsprint to suppress weeds and grass.
  - Thick layers of rocks or gravel.
  - Avoid bark mulch for shoreline plantings (or for access trails to the water), since it can add toxins.
- Weed as often as needed to reduce competition.
- Water every one to two weeks, depending on location and weather conditions.
- Inspect plantings in early spring and replace any that were uprooted by freeze / thaw action over the winter, or severely damaged by rodents.
- Keep an eye on the young plants so that you can detect early signs of disease or insect infestation.

Provide wind and winter protection

Young plants can also be easily damaged by harsh weather conditions. To improve their survival rates:

- If your plantings are in a very windy location, erect a burlap shelter or tie the branches up with garden twine to keep them from breaking.
- Allow snow to build up naturally around the plants to provide winter protection.

5. Deal With Alien Invaders!

Alien invaders are organisms which have been introduced into areas where they are not native, and – as the name implies – can grow out of control. They compete with native species for foods, nutrients, and habitat. Also known as alien invasive species or invasives, they often have no natural enemies and can take over an area. Alien invasive plants can make your shoreline or streamside less attractive for wildlife. They may interfere with boating or swimming. If they spread from your property to that of neighbours, you may find yourself fined under a local weed control bylaw – as well as "alienated" from your neighbours!

Here are some steps you can take to help slow down or reduce the spread of alien invaders.

Become informed

- Learn what invasive species are a problem in your area, and what they look like. *See Appendix 2.*
- Consult with resource people before you try to control or eradicate an invasive species.
- Even areas that are considered "wild" may have alien invasive plants move into them. Walk your property regularly, and keep an eye out for invaders!
- Learn about any native invasive plants ("bully plants") in your area to watch for. (Yes, a few do exist, especially if they are out of balance with other native plants.)

Practise prevention

- Avoid disturbing ground unnecessarily. Once ground is disturbed, alien invasive plants can get a foothold and out-compete native species.
- Plant ground cover immediately after construction or other disturbance of your soil, before weed seeds can get started.

- Watch out for common garden and landscaping plants which may be aggressive in your area. Most alien invasive plants were introduced as landscaping plants. Purple loosestrife, for example, can quickly spread downstream if allowed to go to seed.
- Before you plant any new plant, make sure you know what it is and whether it has the potential to be invasive.
- If you bring a mower from home to the cottage, clean or hose down the blades. You don't want to bring weeds from the city!
- Follow good boating practices to prevent transfer of unwanted species from one water body to another. *See Chapter 14.*

Control methods

⚠️ **CAUTION: It is easy to inadvertently do more harm than good when working with alien invaders.** Check on the best control method for the specific plants you are dealing with. For example, pulling some plants may disturb the soil and expose it to invasion by other plants, or stimulate expansion of roots.

- For plants which can be pulled: pull when young, before their root systems strengthen and make the job harder.

Did you know ...
Invasive plants and animals are considered to be among the most severe, worldwide causes of habitat destruction, loss of biological diversity, and extinction of native species.

> **❝ I was given four small ornamental plants for my garden that were supposed to flower and attract bees. They grew 2 metres high, and have seeded around the pond, which empties into the river. I had no idea they'd be so aggressive and take so much work to keep them under control. ❞**
>
> Shoreline resident

Pour boiling water on cut stem of invasive weeds like dandelion and thistle. After two or three treatments, the plant will weaken and die. Bag any flowering stalks and burn or put into garbage.

Watch your shoelaces! Seeds of invasive species can cling to shoelaces and boot soles, and be transported onto your property.

CAUTION

Do not use old railway ties or telephone poles in your garden or near the shoreline. They are treated with carcinogenic chemicals. Also, be wary of using pressure-treated wood – it can leach arsenic.

- If you are hand pulling, choose a day when the soil is damp from recent rainfall but not soggy. Loosen the plant around the roots and pull carefully, removing as many of the roots as possible. Minimize soil disturbance; gently tread the disturbed soil back down the way a golfer replaces divots.

- If you are trying to control established plants, make sure that you prevent them from flowering and going to seed. You may need to cut or mow twice during the growing season; however, if you choose your timing carefully, they may not flower again for the rest of the season.

- Try boiling water on plants like thistles and dandelion. These have large taproots which form new plants if they break off and remain in the ground. Cut off the plant at the ground, then pour boiling water from a thermos over the exposed cut on the main root stem. This will set the plant back substantially. Repeat the process when the plant resurfaces, and you'll find you gradually weaken it.

- Be thorough. Plants like quack grass have "rhizomes", roots which run underground and connect a series of offshoots. These plants are very difficult to eradicate. Be picky about removing every piece of root/rhizome that you can find.

- Watch seed heads! If you have pulled a weed which has seeds forming, put it head first into a large sturdy plastic bag to prevent further spread. The flowers of some plants, like thistles, will continue to form into seed heads even after pulling.

- Once established, Purple loosestrife and Eurasian milfoil are very difficult to remove from aquatic areas. *See the Resources section at the end for sources of assistance with these invasive species.*

Methods for combatting invasive plant species are always changing. For the latest options, contact Alberta Agriculture, Food and Rural Development or DFO. Some of their methods involve the use of pesticides; because of your proximity to surface water, we strongly suggest you avoid this option. *Read Chapter 14 to learn about invasive aquatic species such as zebra mussels.*

Carefully manage waste

- **NEVER** compost invasive plants. Improper composting will only help their spread.

- If you live in an area where burning is permitted, the waste can be burned. However, some invasive plants use fire as a way of germinating their seeds more quickly. Use a hot fire to kill thoroughly, and dispose of the ashes in the landfill.

- If burning is not an option, place all the waste in sturdy plastic garbage bags and dispose of it in a landfill. Invasives are better off in a landfill than filling the land!

After planting, monitor for alien invaders.

6. Create Wildlife Habitat

For the avid putterer, there are many opportunities to create homes for wildlife – and many good reasons to do it. Most of us who live beside water enjoy listening to the songs of water, shore and songbirds. Gardeners benefit from the fact that birds consume many insects that bother their plants. The fish visit more often when our shorelines are friendly to insects, and lots of fish make happy fishermen! And children are irresistibly drawn to the abundance of life on the shoreline.

Provide a variety of features

You can encourage a diversity of wildlife even if you have only a small space, but you will need to provide a range of habitat features.

- Encourage a diversity of vegetation and mix features like evergreen and deciduous, young and old, tall and short.
- Layer your plants so that the tallest trees are at the edges of your property and drop in size towards your house. Locate shade-tolerant shrubs and ground covers beneath taller trees.
- If your space is restricted, consider planting a clump of trees surrounded by smaller shrubs.
- Create a thicket made up of a small tree surrounded by thick, bushy shrubs. Even in a small area, the different layers and types of vegetation create edges that house an abundance of wildlife.
- Remember, irregular or rounded edges are preferable to straight lines!

Create corridors

Corridors provide safe travel paths for wildlife.

- Connect already existing natural areas by planting between them.
- Allow native vegetation to grow along fence lines or property lines, and use these as corridors to help connect natural areas, or to connect your shoreline area with upland wild areas.
- Work with your neighbours to help create corridors between properties.

Protect dead and downed trees

When trees fall in or along the water, they help protect shorelines and stream banks from erosion. Having a few dead and dying trees along a shoreline is normal and healthy, yet our urban desire to have things look tidy and "nice" makes us want to remove them as soon as they start to lose branches and look diseased.

> **tip**
> *If you are planning a landscaping project and using materials like rock or natural wood (untreated, unpainted, unstained), consider using any leftover materials to create wildlife habitat.*

Did you know . . .

In Alberta, more than 50 species of wildlife, or over 10% of the province's birds, mammals and amphibians, depend on old, dead and decaying trees.

Edges provide wildlife habitat. Create them in your yard by planting a wide variety of plants in groups or thickets.

Did you know . . .

Large dead conifers can remain standing safely for as long as 100 years! They are seldom a blow-down or fire hazard. If you are concerned about a tree, consult an arborist who has taken a wildlife and haz-ardous tree identification course.

> " *I call the deciduous trees between my house and the lake my "green curtain". In summer, when the lake is busy, I have privacy and a lacy view of the water. In fall, winter and spring, the view opens up when the trees lose their leaves.* "
>
> Shoreline resident

Did you know . . .

If you live on a creek, it may be capable of sustaining fish, even if you have never seen a fish in it. Contact Alberta Sustainable Resource Development, Cows and Fish program (Alberta Riparian Habitat Management Program) or DFO for more information on stream restoration.

Decaying or standing dead trees are also wildlife havens, used by mammals, birds, amphibians, and insects as places for a range of activities. As they break down, the trees gradually return nutrients to the soil; in the water, they create pools and provide sources of food for fish and other wildlife.

- Allow a standing dead tree to remain.
- If you are in an urban area, consider making it a feature of a planting with a variety of dense shrubbery around it.
- If you are concerned about safety, rather than felling a tree that is dying or dead, have it trimmed by a tree pruning specialist to a height of 3-4 m (10-13 ft), keeping some branches for perching. You can monitor it for safety over the years.
- When trees fall, let them be. Fallen trees across creeks rarely cause debris jams and flooding.
- If you believe a tree that has fallen in the water presents a safety hazard for boaters or swimmers, contact your fisheries biologist. It may be possible for you to do some trimming and at the same time leave the framework of the tree in place.

Build a wildlife shelter

Instead of hauling branches away, or burning them, pile them in the style of a beaver lodge to provide an instant wildlife sanctuary. You can use extra firewood, rocks or any other natural material you happen to have around to create shelter for birds, small mammals and reptiles. Placed near a favourite feeding area, your shelter will provide safety from predators and a place to get away from the wind.

- You may need to add to the pile as it shrinks over time. Using rocks or logs as a solid foundation will slow the natural decomposition process.
- Leave the pile undisturbed between early spring and early fall when birds may be nesting and using the pile as a safe place to raise their young.
- To provide hiding spots amongst the logs, place clay flower pots on their sides or use bricks, rocks, or clay drain tiles. Cover the

area with leaves and small twigs and disturb as little as possible.
- Both sunbathing reptiles and amphibians enjoy rock piles and dry stone walls (especially if located near water).
- Designing and creating shelters is an ideal project for children to be involved in. And you can show it off to neighbours and visitors when it's finished!

Build a nest box

When spring approaches, cavity-nesting birds struggle to find enough places to lay their eggs, particularly in residential areas, where natural habitat is hard to find.

- You can help compensate for this loss by offering nest boxes for the birds native to your area. As your shoreline plantings grow, these nest boxes will become less necessary.
- You may need to install a protective device on your nest box to limit access by cats and other predators.
- Also consider constructing bat houses for insect-eating bats. *See Chapter 11.*

While nest boxes are helpful for wildlife, encouraging the real thing is better! In your efforts to aid wildlife, a good first step is to preserve and enhance the features on your land that already provide natural nesting sites.

Wildlife habitat projects at the water

Water-based projects to protect shorelines and create wildlife habitat are feasible, but require approvals from Alberta Environment and DFO. Projects such as planting cattails and bulrushes or placing logs in streams help repair degraded habitat. They also help to "soften" your shoreline and prevent erosion on your property. Check with shoreline stabilization or erosion experts or get in touch with a local stream or shoreline stewardship group. They can tell you what is possible and desirable for your shoreline.

7. Soften a Retaining Wall

If you are considering installing a retaining wall along your shoreline, explore the alternatives. Chapter 8 provides information about "soft" shore protection alternatives to solid shorewalls. Retaining walls can actually contribute to shore erosion and worsen problems over the longer term.

As well as interfering with currents along the shore and contributing to erosion, "hardened" shorelines also eliminate the filtering qualities of a natural shoreline, degrade water quality, destroy habitat for fish and wildlife, block wildlife access to and from the water, and scour sand from beaches.

If your reason for installing a retaining wall along your shoreline is to create a flat "useable space" or terrace for outdoor furniture like patio chairs and tables, explore some alternatives. For example, a firepit close to your house may provide you and your family with many hours of enjoyable evening activity. Or, a couple of hammocks under a shady tree in your yard may provide you with more entertainment than an area close to the water's edge. When it comes to planning your outdoor space, think about how you use it most of the time – rather than creating a patio the size of a football field for that block party you might have one day.

If your shoreline has been hardened with rock (often called riprap) or a retaining wall, here are some simple things you can do to "soften" it:

- Restore or plant a strip of deep-rooted vegetation along the retaining wall; this will help filter runoff before it enters the water, and reduce the risk of erosion by holding the soil together.

- Plant overhanging native shrubs to help provide shade and keep water cool. You can also drill planting holes into the wall and plant cuttings or container plants.

- In riprap, plant shrubs in open spaces among the rocks; move rocks if necessary to create space. You can also plant live stakes. *See Chapter 8.*

With approvals from Alberta Environment, Alberta Sustainable Resource Development (SRD) and DFO, there are several things you can do below high water mark:

- Anchor a log or two against a retaining wall to provide some wildlife habitat and help break the force of waves and undercurrents. This will help reduce the scouring action of waves breaking against the wall.

- Add rock riprap to the base of a retaining wall at a forty-five degree angle, to help break the force of waves and improve habitat for fish and wildlife. Gradually sediment may start to deposit among the rocks, and aquatic plants may grow.

- Create shore "ladders" of riprap from the base of the wall to the top. These will help provide wildlife (such as amphibians) access from the water to the land.

Consider replacing an existing retaining wall with a more shore-friendly structure. It is possible to dig out the backfill behind the wall, remove or break up the wall, regrade the slope, and plant vegetation. Obtain professional advice to avoid further damage to the shoreline, and obtain approvals from Alberta Environment, SRD and DFO.

Did you know . . .
Breakwaters and retaining walls can transfer the energy of waves and currents along a shoreline, causing erosion farther along the shore – on your own property or a neighbour's.

tip **To plant in a riprap slope, create planting pockets between rocks by moving them apart with a pry bar. Pierce any filter fabric found underneath to give plant roots access to the soil below. Plant container, bare root, or live stakes, depending on the time of year.** *See Chapter 8.*

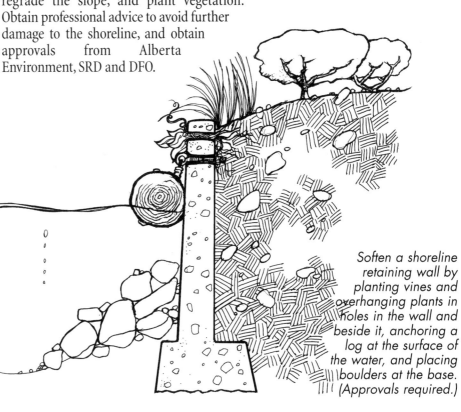
Soften a shoreline retaining wall by planting vines and overhanging plants in holes in the wall and beside it, anchoring a log at the surface of the water, and placing boulders at the base. (Approvals required.)

8. Clean Up Garbage, Leave Natural Debris

Many of us like to clear away the things that float up onto our beaches, or get caught in shrubs and grasses on the shore. But what is truly garbage, and what should we leave? Streams and shorelines are on the receiving end of debris floating downstream, pushed and carried by waves and currents. For the most part, rocks, logs, plants, and aquatic vegetation help protect your shore from erosion, and provide food and habitat for wildlife. The general rule is to leave them in place if you can.

- Leave logs, branches and trees that have washed up on your shoreline or beach, or fallen in a creek. Resist collecting logs for firewood – they are essential to protecting your shoreline from erosion!

- Leave rocks in the water. If you need to move a rock for safety purposes, or to protect boat bottoms, move it by hand. Heavy machinery can do a lot of damage to the shoreline.

- If you have lots of material like dried reeds and logs along your shoreline, build a walkway over them, or create a narrow path through them to access the water.

- Refrain from clearing debris in your buffer zone. Trees that topple, or branches that fall off, all help contribute to a healthy buffer area.

  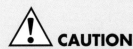 Do remove human-made garbage like styrofoam, plastic bags, glass, cans when you find them. Garbage can harm wildlife and their habitat, interfere with recreation along the shore, foul boat motors – and it's ugly!

- Take care when removing junk like tires, concrete slabs, or old cars and other metals. They may contain toxic substances or be dangerous, and the process of pulling them out of water can cause environmental damage, stirring up sediments and altering currents. Consult with your local Alberta Environment or DFO officials first.

---

tip *Talk to your neighbours about your shoreline restoration project. It may be mutually beneficial – especially if they have erosion problems or invasive plants that are affecting your property. You'll be an ambassador for healthy shorelines!*

⚠️ **CAUTION**

Never push piles of tree branches, grass clippings, or leaves over banks into creeks or lakes. When we add extra organic matter to rivers and lakes, we overload them.

Resources

Fact Sheet on Riparian Restoration. www-heb.pac.dfo-mpo.gc.ca/english/programs/hcsp/links/PDF%20files/Riparian%20Revegetation.pdf

Links to restoration websites. www-heb.pac.dfo-mpo.gc.ca/english/programs/hcsp/links/lkhm.htm#restoration

NatureScape Alberta. 2000. Pearman, Myrna and Ted Pike. Red Deer River Naturalists. Red Deer, Alberta.

Alberta Native Plant Council. www.anpc.ab.ca

Lakescaping for Wildlife and Water Quality. 2000. Henderson, Carrol L. et al. Department of Natural Resources. St. Paul, Minnesota.

How to Get Your Lawn off Grass. 2002. Rubin, Carole. Harbour Publishing. Madeira Park, British Columbia.

See Appendix 1 for complete Resources.

8 Shoreline Erosion

Losing Your Land

*T*he springfed lake we live on is so small that we rarely even see whitecaps. Perhaps we have become a wee bit complacent thinking that erosion will never be at the top of our issue list. But just over the hill, on the "big lake", and in the valley beside the river, it's a different story. Countless times we have seen, and heard about, erosion nightmares... grassy banks collapsing into streams, or retaining walls which begin crumbling after only a few years. Even small events like boat wakes can cause grief; one friend loses a bit of her bank each year during high water, whenever boats go by.*

Questions about preventing or correcting erosion problems are among those most frequently asked by shoreline residents. Whether you live by a small stream that becomes a raging torrent after a heavy rainfall, a tranquil lake that picks up big waves when the wind is right, or at the top of a bluff which slumps a little more every year, erosion is a fact of life. Throughout this chapter, when we talk about the "erosion zone", we especially mean the tops of bluffs, banks, or ravines, as well as the place where water meets land, your true shore line. These are the places where your property is most susceptible to erosive forces.

Erosion Blues

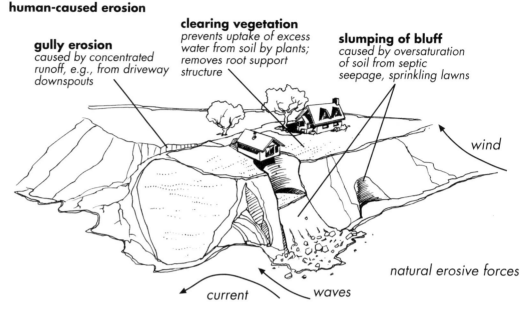

human-caused erosion

gully erosion
caused by concentrated runoff, e.g., from driveway downspouts

clearing vegetation
prevents uptake of excess water from soil by plants; removes root support structure

slumping of bluff
caused by oversaturation of soil from septic seepage, sprinkling lawns

wind

natural erosive forces

current *waves*

 CAUTION
When you buy property along a shoreline or in a flood plain, be aware of the risks of erosion and runoff associated with your location.

Erosion can translate into substantial losses by reducing the value and productivity of our properties. Some of us know unlucky folks who have lost property to the power of water, or whose homes have been threatened by a rapidly eroding bluff or bank.

The gradual wearing away of land surfaces due to factors such as water, ice and wind is a natural process; erosion creates the beaches, bluffs and floodplains that we love.

However, we can accelerate erosion and create problems for ourselves and our neighbours with some of the things we do on our land, along our shorelines, and below the high water mark.

By being aware of erosion risks and taking appropriate action, you will be better armed to help safeguard your property and protect your pocketbook.

One of the most damaging things we do is to remove native vegetation, rocks and logs from our shorelines, banks or bluffs. These elements provide a very strong natural line of defence. Once they're gone, the land is exposed and becomes more vulnerable to becoming an erosion zone. Remember, the secret of success is keeping it natural – the beauty of the buffer! Once erosion has begun, planting to protect the shoreline, bank or bluff from further erosion can become difficult, and sometimes costly.

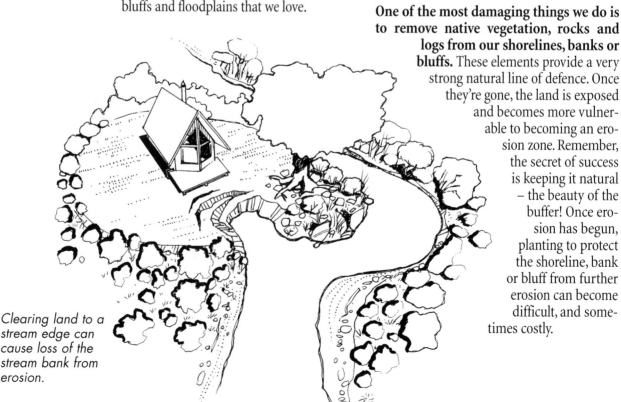

Clearing land to a stream edge can cause loss of the stream bank from erosion.

Assessing Potential Erosion

By assessing the erosion potential of your property, you may be able to prevent erosion problems before they occur.

Setbacks The farther buildings are from the water's edge, the more protected they will be from erosion. If a building is too close to the edge of a bluff or bank, it may be cheaper in the long run to move the building back, than to attempt to stop erosion with structures like retaining walls. Then you can explore alternative ways of managing erosion (such as improving drainage or planting vegetation along the bluff's crest).

⚠ **CAUTION: *If you have any concerns about a receding shoreline, consult with a geotechnical engineer.***

Slope Usually, the steeper the grade, the more likely the slope will suffer from erosion.

Soil Rocky shores are unlikely to erode very quickly; but if a clay or silt shoreline has started to erode, it can be a challenge to reverse the process.

Shoreline features If there are signs of past instability, such as slumping or landslides, you may face similar problems in the future.

Vegetation Is the shoreline well covered with substantial natural vegetation such as mature trees, shrubs and grasses that help stabilize slopes?

Neighbours Do neighbouring properties have retaining walls, signs of eroded banks or slumpage such as exceptionally bare tree roots, bare areas without vegetation, or gullies? Their problems could be passed on to you.

Location If the prevailing wind blows waves into the shoreline or bluff you may find increased erosion potential from wave action, especially during stormy weather.

Water levels What are current water levels in relation to the historical range of water levels? Changes in water level have an impact on the water table and can destabilize banks.

Natural beach Where is the beach in relation to the high water mark? Is it a natural beach? Beaches made of imported sand will, in most cases, eventually be carried away by the water.

Drainage Can you see water seeping from the side of the slope, or evidence of drainage and runoff over the surface of the property? Slumping and erosion are more likely in soil that is saturated with moisture.

Bluffs Is the toe of the bluff subject to wave attack? If so, what is the nature and frequency of wave action? Small waves acting over time can potentially do as much damage as one severe storm.

Did you know . . . A setback of 60 m (200 ft) plus the height of the slope may be suggested in areas where the shoreline is receding by 50 cm (20 in) per year.

Did you know . . . The dirt that enters surface water from runoff and erosion can:
- destroy plant habitat for aquatic creatures by blocking sunlight
- increase costs of drinking water treatment
- make swimming less enjoyable
- cover fish spawning beds

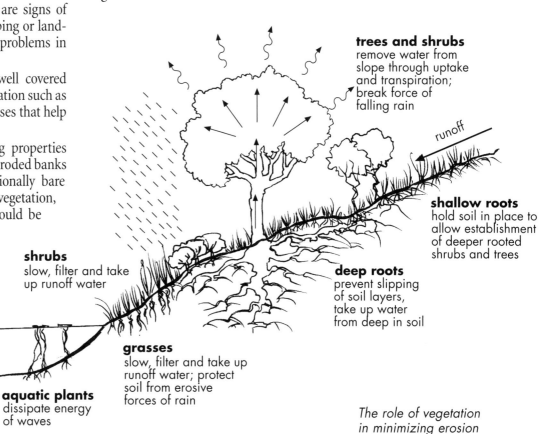

trees and shrubs remove water from slope through uptake and transpiration; break force of falling rain

runoff

shallow roots hold soil in place to allow establishment of deeper rooted shrubs and trees

deep roots prevent slipping of soil layers, take up water from deep in soil

shrubs slow, filter and take up runoff water

grasses slow, filter and take up runoff water; protect soil from erosive forces of rain

aquatic plants dissipate energy of waves

The role of vegetation in minimizing erosion on a shoreline

Preventing Erosion

⚠️ **CAUTION**

Watch out for heavy fines! Under the Federal Fisheries Act you may have to pay fines of up to $300,000, cover the cost of repairing any shoreline damage or even take a trip to jail for causing damage to fish habitat.

Erosion is a complex phenomenon that can be caused by factors such as waves and currents undercutting bluffs and banks, groundwater seepage causing bluffs to slump, and surface runoff creating gullies down slopes. Before you take action to deal with an erosion problem, examine these interrelated forces at work on your property. Looking at the big picture will give you a better idea of how to proceed and increase your chances of success.

Similarly, before clearing your land and starting construction, evaluate what impact your project will have on drainage and runoff. Remember, the best (and least expensive!) defence against future erosion is to leave shorelines, banks and the tops of bluffs in their natural state.

- Retain vegetation. It helps absorb potential runoff and excess moisture within the soil.
- Avoid adding weight (buildings, parking areas) close to the edge of bluffs and banks; it may cause slumping.

- Manage site drainage. *Review the tips in Chapter 4.* Many erosion problems can be traced to improper drainage as a result of construction.
- Be cautious when employing heavy equipment; an excavator or backhoe can destroy a shoreline in just a few minutes of work. To restore its intricate ecosystem may take years.
- Evaluate – before you build – whether a shoreline access trail might cause erosion or instability in a slope. *See Chapter 9.*
- Build a dock which will allow the free flow of currents along the shoreline. *See Chapter 9.*

⚠️ **CAUTION: *Before you consider making any changes to the shoreline or to existing shore protection installations, obtain professional advice and check with DFO.***

First Aid for Erosion Problems

Erosion problems can vary from small amounts of soil being washed away during a rainstorm, to disastrously slumping banks or disappearing shoreline frontage. Assessing the severity and cause of your problem can be complicated. Sometimes factors upstream, or along the shore, play a significant role. If you are in any doubt about what is contributing to your problem, we recommend a consultation with a specialist who focusses on shoreline erosion. Geotechnical, civil or soil bioengineers may be able to assist.

For solutions to your problems, choose a professional who is familiar with "soft shore protection", also called "soft armouring" or "soil bioengineering". Even if your problem appears to be fairly minor, for peace of mind, it is likely worth the cost of a consultation with someone who is knowledgeable. Choosing the wrong approach can be an expensive, time-consuming and sometimes damaging mistake!

This section contains a brief explanation of some of the more commonly used approaches to erosion control. It will give you somewhere to begin discussions with the various professionals you contact, and provide you with knowledge for informed decision-making. It will also help you get started on some small do-it-yourself erosion control projects that can have positive results.

Remember, methods for protecting shorelines usually require some maintenance. Include these maintenance costs in your budget.

Plan ahead

In addition to obtaining professional advice, you will need to consult with, and obtain approvals from, Fisheries and Oceans Canada (DFO), Alberta Sustainable Resource Development (SRD) and Alberta Environment for any work below the high water mark. If your work involves major impacts to the area above the high water mark, you may also need to consult with these agencies, and possibly your local municipality, or any designated covenant holder.

The more information that you provide about your project, the easier it will be for officials to review it. Give yourself – and government officials – lots of planning and review time. You will need to plan construction work to avoid sensitive times for fish and other wildlife.

The best windows of opportunity for construction vary from location to location, depending on factors such as what fish species and other wildlife use your shore, seasonal cycles, runoff patterns, etc. If there is a citizen's group or non-government organization in your area involved in shoreline restoration projects, you may want to contact them as well for assistance.

If you have steep, bare slopes along your shoreline, you may need to cut them back to flatter angles, before you can install erosion prevention measures and achieve slopes suitable for planting. Most erosion control methods work best with a maximum slope of 50%, or 1:2 (vertical:horizontal). However, you may still be able to plant a steeper slope using more complex soil bioengineering techniques.

Estimating the slope of your shoreline

Choose a stretch of slope that is representative of your shoreline.

* Pound in a short stake at the top of the slope and a long stake about 1.5 m (5 ft) high roughly 8 to 10 m (25–30 ft) downhill; string the line between the two to form a 90 degree angle, as shown. (Use a carpenter's level on the line.)
* Measure the vertical distance up the long stake to the point at which the line comes in on the perpendicular, and measure the horizontal distance crossed by the line.
* Use the following calculation to calculate the slope:

$$\frac{\text{vertical distance}}{\text{horizontal distance}} \times 100\% = \text{slope}$$

For example:

$$\frac{1.5 \text{ metres}}{10 \text{ metres}} \times 100\% = 15\% \text{ slope}$$

 CAUTION

While you have the right as a waterfront landowner to construct works on your property to protect it from erosion, any construction in or adjacent to the water will likely require approvals by a variety of agencies.

See Chapter 17.

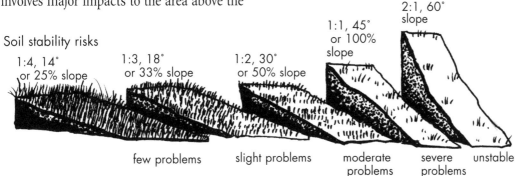

Soil stability risks

1:4, 14°
or 25% slope

1:3, 18°
or 33% slope

1:2, 30°
or 50% slope

1:1, 45°
or 100%
slope

2:1, 60°
slope

few problems   slight problems   moderate problems   severe problems   unstable

Soft Shore Protection

tip *Check with local conservation groups that do shoreline restoration work. You may be able to get help with your shoreline stabilization project.*

Seeding

good for:
- Areas with mild erosion problems
- Stabilizing until shrubs or trees can take root
- Can be used in combination with other techniques

advantages:
- Relatively easy, quick and inexpensive
- Technique is compatible with many slope situations

disadvantages:
- Not adequate for highly eroded areas
- Vegetation can take longer to become established than when seedlings or cuttings are used

In the last few years, as soil bioengineering research and restoration work have expanded, erosion experts are learning that the most successful and least costly approaches to dealing with erosion problems involve mimicking nature's own designs, and using native vegetation as much as possible. Soft shore protection, or soil bioengineering, combines plants and other materials (rocks, logs) to create a "living barrier" of protection. This barrier controls erosion and runoff, increases the stability of slopes, and at the same time helps to maintain and improve habitat for wildlife. And it blends into the surroundings, creating a natural look.

Soft shore techniques rely on the binding action of native plant roots; plants adapt to changing shoreline conditions and become stronger as they mature. The roots of species used in soil bioengineering often strengthen after stems are damaged (by a storm, for example). Traditional erosion control techniques that involve building barriers of concrete or stone sometimes suffer damage very quickly from waves and wind, become weakened or undermined, and eventually collapse.

Many of the materials used in soil bioengineering can be obtained locally and installed with light equipment, saving you the cost and potential damage by heavy machines.

If you want to carry out some small erosion control projects yourself, we recommend combining seeding with planting live stakes, container and bare root plants. In steeper locations consider using live palisades *(see Pg 73)* in combination with rocks and logs for practical and aesthetic purposes.

Choose native species

Trees, shrubs and perennials that are adapted for the climate and growing conditions of your area are essential to making soft shore protection work. Native plants appropriate for the site (e.g., willows for wet shoreline areas or snowberry on drier upland slopes) will root easily, grow well and require little maintenance once they're established. They will also ready the site for other native plants which tend to move in after a few years, as happens in nature. For example, poplar might gradually move into an area where native grasses and shrubs have been growing.

Interest in native plants has grown substantially over recent years, and there are now many places to find information. *See Chapter 7 and Appendix 2 for some tips about selecting and growing native plants. For sources of plants suitable for your area and site conditions, ask at your local nursery, your local agriculture office, or see Contacts and Resources for the Alberta Native Plant Council website.*

Seeding

Seeding involves the hand planting of native grasses and perennials whose quick growing roots help bind surface soils and protect them from runoff, wind and other erosive forces. Use it for temporary protection while other methods take hold, and in conjunction with larger shrubs and trees. Your planting may need the extra protection of biodegradable landscape fabric or matting, especially if it extends down a slope. It may also need a regular supply of water, especially in the vulnerable first year.

Hand Sowing

Uniformly scatter seeds by hand, making sure your seeds stay near the soil surface. (Planting depth is determined by type of seed.) Mulch immediately with straw, newspaper, jute netting or similar material to help retain moisture, and to prevent soil and seed from being washed away or eaten by birds and wildlife.

For a large area that may be subject to erosion, consider hydroseeding. This involves spraying a combination of seed, water, a "sticking" agent and mulch onto the soil. Avoid chemical fertilizers in the mix. Be sure to check that the source of seed is appropriate for your location, and monitor contractors to ensure there is no overspray into the water.

"Drilling" Holes

This method is best used on shallow slopes, smaller areas, and for woody plant stock. It is essentially the same technique you would use when planting a garden. Make holes to a depth required by the particular seed type and ensure that the soil surrounding each hole is loosened so that root systems can develop. Place several seeds in each hole and water.

Container and bare root planting

This method involves placing container-grown or bare root (for example, transplanted) native plants into dug holes.

Finding plants

You can obtain plants by rescuing them from sites under development, starting them from seeds or cuttings, or buying from a local native plant nursery. Nursery stock is convenient and gives quicker results than growing from seed or cuttings, but may cost more.

⚠️ **CAUTION: *Never dig up native species from the wild unless the area is about to be cleared or treated with pesticide (for example, under power lines).*** Always check with the property owner first.

- Choose healthy plants that are at least two years old, native to your area and elevation, and of species appropriate for your site. *Check the species listing in Appendix 2.*
- Trees and bushes leaving the nursery can suffer transplant shock, so be ready to baby them.
- Store your plants in a cool, shady place before planting, and keep the roots moist.

Ten easy steps to planting

Plant bare root seedlings before leaf buds appear in the spring or after the leaves have dropped in the fall. Container-grown plants can be planted up to early summer or in the autumn before the leaves fall. Planting in spring is often the best choice because it helps give the roots a full season to become established.

1. Pick a cool, damp day with little wind, or plant in the evening; the plants will be less stressed.
2. Plant shrubs in clusters with other shrubs or trees, between 60-100 cm (24-40 in) apart on all sides. Planting in groups improves survival rates.
3. For each planting, dig a hole that is two to three times larger than the size of the roots. Loosen 20 cm (8 in) of soil at the bottom and the sides of the hole, and mix in a little bone meal and some organic material like peat moss or compost.

4. When working with container plants, gently untangle the roots. If the roots are pot-bound and encircling the pot, snip some of them.
5. Mound some soil in the middle of the hole for roots to form around.
6. Place the plant upright in the middle of the hole, making sure the roots are not bent upwards. Bury the plant so the top of the rootball is flush with the soil.
7. Fill in two-thirds of the hole. Carefully pack down the soil. Finish filling the hole and press firmly to ensure that there are no air pockets. Build a berm (a dirt wall) around the plant to hold water, unless the tree or shrub is one that tolerates dry conditions. This is critical on slopes.
8. Water (unless your soil is saturated).
9. Cut off any dead or broken branches.
10. Mulch with straw, newspaper, or comparable material. Do not mulch right up to the main stem of the shrub or tree. *For tips on maintaining shrubs and trees after planting, refer to Chapter 7.*

Live staking and live palisades

Live staking involves putting live stakes (also called cuttings or whips) of native woody plants into the ground to root and grow. Live palisades are living fences of thick stakes (often balsam poplar) planted deep into the ground to help stabilize an eroding bank. The easiest plants to propagate from cuttings are willows, dogwoods and poplars.

Container and bare root planting

good for:
- Areas that need immediate assistance. Deeper roots provide more stabilization than grasses.

advantages:
- Planting rooted plant materials gives you a head start; makes for faster stabilization, has a higher plant success rate.
- Easy to put into place.

disadvantages:
- Can be expensive.
- Takes some planning, and more long term care.

 To prevent erosion when watering new plants on slopes:
- **Mulch.**
- **Build berms or small dams of rock or soil around plants to hold water.**
- **Use a fine spray when watering.**

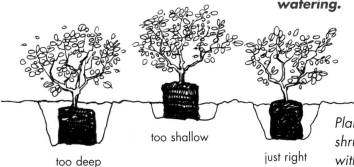

too deep

too shallow

just right

Plant any seedling, shrub or tree flush with the top of its root ball.

good for:

- Gentle slopes and flat areas; live palisades may be suitable for steeper sites.
- Small eroded areas and wet areas with slumps.
- Can be used alone or with other planting techniques.

advantages:

- Easy, inexpensive, and can be planted with minimal surface preparation or disturbance.
- Helps reduce slope soil moisture and stabilize slopes by creating a root system that holds soil and extracts moisture.
- Requires little maintenance once installed.

disadvantages:

- Ineffective on deep erosion problems and slope instabilities, except live palisades can be used beside steeper banks as a back armour or secondary defence.

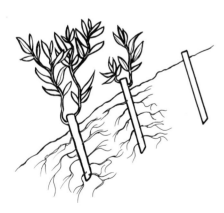

As a live stake of native willow, dogwood or poplar grows, its roots act like rebar in concrete to help to stabilize an eroding shoreline.

Obtaining cuttings

Take cuttings from fully dormant plants on sites that are similar to yours. If you are collecting many cuttings, collect them from over a wide area to ensure genetic variety in your stock and avoid stressing any one plant. For cuttings to be planted in areas where they will have to compete with weeds or grasses, or which become dry in summer, use thick branches about the diameter of fence posts. Otherwise, cut your stakes 70 – 100 cm (2 – 3 ft) long, and at least 2.5 cm (1 in) in diameter. For palisades cut stakes at least 2 m (6 ft) long and up to 15 cm (6 in) in diameter, depending on the difficulty of the erosion control task.

Cutting the bottom at an angle makes it easier to push or drive the live stake into the ground and also helps mark the bottoms; however, the cut exposes a larger area, so it will tend to dry out faster. You can also mark the tops with latex paint diluted in water, or by bundling them in one direction and flagging.

Store the cuttings in plastic bags (with ventilation to prevent mould growth) in a refrigerator or a snow bank until you are ready to plant them. Soak cuttings in water for one to ten days before planting to help them survive dry conditions.

Planting

The best time to plant is during the spring while the plant material is still dormant. Consult your local nursery, or obtain assistance from a local conservation group, to find out the recommended spacing and other planting requirements for each species.

The planting pattern you choose for live staking will likely depend on the number of cuttings you have, the size of the area you are planting, and the severity of the erosion problem. Plant your cuttings 30 – 90 cm (12 – 36 in) from each other. Keep willows closer together than poplars. If too many cuttings survive and start crowding each other, or shade the water too much, thin some out.

To plant a cutting, make a hole the correct diameter using a hammer or mallet to pound a stake (such as a piece of rebar or a pry bar) into the ground. Then, push or use a rubber mallet to gently tap your live cutting into the

hole. You can place a piece of wood or a metal cap across the top of the cutting to prevent splitting. Bury cuttings three-quarters of their length on wet sites and seven-eighths of their length on drier sites, leaving the rest exposed. Sufficient depth is very important, to encourage the cutting to produce more roots.

When constructing a live palisade fence, dig a trench 2-3 m (6-10 ft) below the top of the eroding slope. The trench must be deep enough so the cuttings extend down to the water level (they need a water source) and stick out at least 1 m (3 ft) above ground. As you fill in the trench, plant cuttings from a variety of species to provide diversity.

If you have an actively eroding shoreline, you may need to use erosion control blankets, mulches, and landscape fabrics to help retain your soil while your plantings are taking root. Consult with experts to ensure you take advantage of the most up-to-date information. There are many specialized materials being developed.

Using rocks and logs

Rocks and logs are an integral part of a soil bioengineering approach – an approach that's really about following Mother Nature's example. When a tree falls onto a bank and into the water, it acts as a nursery for many plant and wildlife species as it decays. It also stabilizes the shoreline and bank by obstructing the movement of runoff and the action of waves on the shore. By placing logs (anchoring them if necessary) in strategic locations we can take a page from nature's book – protect the shoreline and make it look beautiful too.

Cleverly placed rocks can save banks at drainage outfalls or in gullies, break the force of waves and provide a place for fish and other wildlife to take shelter and feed. Rocks and logs can help to anchor plantings, speeding up the naturalization of your shoreline and giving you more green, more quickly.

Extreme Erosion Problems

There may be cases where standard soil bio-engineering techniques alone are not enough to handle the erosion on your site. If the erosion is already severe, or the wear is ongoing, soil bioengineering techniques may need the support of some "harder" solutions.

Hard armour using human-made structures alone such as solid concrete or heavy rocks or rock in wire cages (called gabions) used to be the erosion control method of choice. Experience has shown that hard armouring is difficult to implement successfully, and if poorly designed or improperly constructed, may be worse than leaving the problem alone! This approach is generally more expensive than soft shore techniques – it often requires the use of heavy equipment – and is more likely to damage the surrounding environment. It is also more difficult to obtain approvals.

If you are considering the hard armour option, it is essential to have your project designed and carried out by an engineer or someone with considerable expertise in the area. Without a competent engineer, hard armouring carries with it the risk of making costly, hard-to-reverse mistakes. Consult with the Association of Professional Engineers, Geologists and Geophysicists of Alberta (APEGGA) for a suitable experienced professional. If your project causes problems for your neighbour, you could be on the receiving end of legal action! *See the tips in Chapter 4 for hiring a contractor.*

If you and your engineer decide to go with hard armouring, you can still have a green, habitat-friendly shoreline. There are many techniques for planting in and over a hard structure that may even increase its effectiveness. For example, there are now "green gabion" techniques that mix a "hard" approach with live plantings. *See Chapter 7, Soften a Retaining Wall, for ideas.*

If you already have a retaining wall or other form of hardened shoreline, consider "retiring" it, to help improve habitat and restore shoreline function. *See sidebar.*

If you have an erosion situation, some of the steps you might consider to help assess it and develop a solution include the following:

- Check the Living by Water website for references: www.livingbywater.ca
- Call the Planning Department in your municipality and talk to an Environmental Planner.
- Talk to a biologist at your local Alberta Environment office.
- Talk to a geotechnical engineer. They often have the expertise to determine the underlying cause of your erosion problem.
- Talk to a soil bioengineering specialist. They can help with finding a cost-effective and shore-friendly solution.
- If you have a very challenging problem that involves a possible threat to your safety or to your property, call a civil engineer. Ask if they have shoreline erosion experience and if they would be prepared to work with you and look at a soil bioengineering approach. As with hiring any contractor, check out qualifications and get more than one opinion.
- In an emergency that involves threat to human life or property call your local police or fire department.

Note: This chapter is intended as a general guide to help you make better decisions and to assist you in talking to the right professionals. It is not intended as advice on any specific erosion situation.

tip **To remove a retaining wall:**
- **Obtain approvals and professional advice.**
- **Dig out the supporting backfill behind wall.**
- **Regrade the slope to 1:2 (vertical to horizontal) and cover with erosion control fabric.**
- **Break up and either haul away the concrete wall or place small pieces on the new slope.**
- **Plant native grasses and shrubs in the spaces.**

Resources

Soil Bioengineering.
www.on.ec.gc.ca/doc/cuf_factsheets/soil-bioeng-e.html

Slope Stabilization and Erosion Control Using Vegetation. 1993.93-30
www.ecy.wa.gov/programs/sea/pubs/93-30

Vegetation Management: A Guide for Puget Sound Bluff Property Owners. 1993.93-31
www.ecy.wa.gov/programs/sea/pubs/93-31/intro.html

Surface Water and Groundwater on Coastal Bluffs. 1995.95-107
www.ecy.wa.gov/programs/sea/pubs/95-107/intro.html

Understanding, Living with, and Controlling Shoreline Erosion. A Guidebook for Shoreline Property Owners. 1997. Fuller, Douglas. Tip of the Mitt Watershed Council. Conway, Michigan.
www.watershedcouncil.org/shore.htm

See Appendix 1 for complete Resources.

9 Accessing the Water

Trails, Beaches and Docks

W*hen we ran the resort, the first thing guests would do when they arrived, sometimes hot and irritable from a long drive, was to pour out of the car and head to the lake. We wanted to make sure that people could access the water safely and easily. By focussing access in only a few areas, we were able to protect most of our shoreline from damage and trampling – and help keep our natural buffer working.*

The low-impact solutions for accessing the shore that we recommend in this chapter are time and money savers – whether you summer by the shore, run a bed and breakfast, or have a fifty foot lot with a creek at the back. The solutions are often simple to construct, easier to get permits for, and last a long time (helping you save on repair and replacement costs). And you'll avoid setting up the conditions that can lead to erosion on your shoreline.

Any kind of regular access through your buffer to the water's edge can have an impact on the sensitive soils and fragile banks which often are associated with shorelines. With a little planning and some creative thinking, you will be able to keep negative effects to a minimum and allow the shoreline, and wildlife, to thrive.

Trails

Building a shoreline access trail will allow you to direct how you and your visitors use the shoreline. Focussing foot traffic in one carefully chosen area will help minimize impacts. It will also protect your buffer zone and let it continue to do its work of safeguarding your property and surface water.

When you build a trail to access the shoreline, take into account any other plans you have for shoreline development, particularly dock structures. Concentrate your shoreline alterations in one area. By doing so, you will reduce the size of "puncture" in your buffer zone – and preserve its ability to work for you. Your trail will have the least impact if you follow these general design considerations:

- Avoid a steep path that cuts straight down a bank or bluff to the water. Such a path can be difficult or even dangerous to navigate, and can create a source of erosion which flushes silt into the water. Use gently angled, S-curve switchbacks instead.

- On steep slopes, build stairs with landings instead of a path to access the waterfront. (Approvals will be required even if the structure just overhangs the Crown owned bed and shore. *See Chapter 17.*) Stairs make shoreline access easier and safer, help your shoreline withstand frequent use, and decrease erosion. Strategically placed landings also give you a place to rest and enjoy the view. Be careful in areas prone to moving ice, however, since stairs anchored to the slope can be pulled out, damaging the entire slope.

- Put your stair support stringers on concrete pilings to keep the wood from contacting the ground. You can purchase easy-to-use cardboard "forms" from your local builders' supply store. These can be left in the ground to gradually biodegrade after the concrete has been poured. This approach reduces the amount of cutting into the slope or bank which is necessary. *See Chapter 4 for erosion control measures during construction.*

- Add a step or two in any location on the trail, especially where the slope is greater than 10%.

- Build a boardwalk 10-50 cm (4-20 in) over shoreline vegetation or sand dunes, rather than clearing and placing fill.

- Leave 4 cm (1.5 in) between planks to allow water to drain, and leaves and needles to fall through.

- To keep boardwalks from getting slippery, use non-slip paint or secure non-skid treads, pieces of asphalt roof shingle, or galvanized mesh on the walking surface.

Did you know ... As a waterfront property owner, you have the right to access the water for the purpose of navigation. See Chapter 17.

Build trails and docks to avoid cutting into the bank. Every time you cut the shoreline, you expose it to potential erosion.

Did you know ... Personal transporters are available which move people down a slope on a rail system.

⚠️ **CAUTION**

On very steep slopes, stair construction may destabilize the terrain. Consider alternate ways of access the shore – e.g., by trail elsewhere, shared with neighbours.

Minimize damage to a slope by supporting stairs on narrow concrete posts poured into cardboard forms and elevated above vegetation.

Beaches

CAUTION

Alberta Sustainable Resource Development (SRD) must authorize any permanent structure on the bed, shore, or floodplain of a lake, river, or stream. Alterations to water bodies by dredging, or placing sand or fill, need to be approved by Alberta Environment and Fisheries and Oceans Canada (DFO). Municipal development permits may also be required for shoreline construction.

Make sure a swimming platform is visible to boaters and clear of busy traffic areas. You may need approvals from the Canadian Coast Guard.
See Chapter 17.

Often, our mental picture of a perfect waterfront paradise includes a Hawaii-like beach of golden sand. How many of us have kept ourselves going through long winter nights with thoughts of a mellow summer afternoon, soaking up some sunshine, and watching our children or grandchildren make sandcastles? The reality is, however, that only a small percentage of waterfront properties in Canada are endowed with a natural beach; the sand of our dreams may need to be somewhere other than beside the water.

The costs of importing sand

Before you clear your shoreline to create a beach, consider the following:

- An artificial beach will disappear; waves, currents, ice and other erosive forces always work to remove sand over time. Even pulling up your boat, or walking on sloping sand constantly, can push the sand from an artificial beach downhill and into the water.

- By adding more sand to an eroding beach, you risk gradually filling in your favourite waterway, silting the habitat of fish and other animals – and possibly damaging the quality of your drinking water.

- Imported sand (especially unwashed building sand) can bring hitchhikers with it – unwanted little critters and seeds that may be inappropriate for your area.

- When you clear shoreline vegetation to create space for a beach, you lose one of your critical means of runoff and erosion control, as well as habitat for wildlife.

- All land below the high water line or "natural boundary" (bank) of a water body belongs to the Crown and is public land. If you alter it without prior approval, you may find yourself facing prosecution, perhaps after a neighbour has tipped off local authorities!

Beach alternatives

It is possible to obtain a waterfront "beach experience" without harming valuable natural shoreline. Here are some possibilities to consider:

- Anchor a swimming platform offshore to give yourself a "floating beach".

- Construct a low-impact dock and narrow shoreline access trail. These will give you many of the same amenities as a beach of imported sand.

- Create a small landscaped beach above the highwater mark; sand is much more likely to stay in place there. Landscape it with logs, rocks, and native plants suitable for your area, and you'll avoid the need for watering.

- Build a sandbox near the house or cottage for young children; you will be able to keep an eye on them more easily than if they were at the water's edge! If you build it under a shade tree, you'll have the added bonus of not having to worry about them getting sunburn.

If your existing imported sand beach is gradually eroding, you'll fight a losing battle if you bring in more sand to maintain it. Instead, let nature take its course: allow native vegetation to grow back, and watch your buffer restore itself. Then, use a few of the ideas above to regain your "beach experience".

A small landscaped beach above the high water mark can be aesthetic, and meet your recreational needs.

Docks

Before beginning a dock project, do some research and planning. Evaluate your needs and whether there are alternative ways to meet them. You can save a lot of capital investment, and prevent shoreline damage, by making use of existing structures and facilities instead of building your own. If your primary need is for somewhere to moor a boat, consider the following:

- Would a mooring buoy or boatlift, which is cheaper and has far less environmental impact than a dock, be sufficient?
- Maybe you have access to public moorage, a nearby marina, or a neighbour's dock.
- Check whether a community dock is being planned for your area.
- Explore whether using a public boat ramp to access water would work for you. Trailering your boat gives you flexibility and is very cost efficient.
- If you are considering making a substantial investment in a dock, make sure you are committed to using your boat.

If you decide to go ahead with your dock structure, contact SRD for dock construction guidelines, as the size, orientation, location and design of the dock play a major role in obtaining approval to build. See *The Application Process* at the end of the chapter. Also check with your local municipality, as some have bylaws regulating docks.

Begin your planning by sketching your shoreline and identifying its main features, including property lines, high water mark (*see Chapter 17*), topography and vegetation along the shore. Consider also the **substrate** (land under the water – rock, sand, mud), the location of submerged navigational hazards, and direction of prevailing winds. If the property is too exposed, a dock may not be feasible.

Choosing a dock

A dock has to work in relation to the shoreline and the body of water on which it is built. You will want your investment to last as long as possible and withstand the forces of nature (wind, pounding waves, ice, aquatic vegetation and animals). Since your dock will likely have to be removed each fall, it must also be easy to move and store. If you design it in isolation of its environment, your dock may not last. In addition, it could cause water quality and erosion problems and affect aquatic life in many ways.

Potential impacts

- Unsuitable dock designs may produce erosion and silting by changing water flows.
- Dock piles and supports can damage shoreline plants and disturb soils, increasing the risk of erosion and invasion by non-native species, and making the area unsuitable for its native inhabitants.
- Permanent docks and supports can be hazardous to snowmobiles and other wintertime users.

Design

- Avoid any plan which will require you to use fill or dredge. In general, approving agencies will not permit these activities.
- Build a dock that allows the free flow of water beneath it.
- To ensure as long a life as possible, design your dock so that loads are spread evenly over the structure.
- Choose a design which permits public access along the shore below the high water mark and that doesn't interfere with navigation.
- If possible locate post-supported docks on a hard substrate such as rocks or gravel.

Style

- Select a style of dock which minimizes disturbance to the water body floor. Post-supported, cantilever and floating docks are generally preferred over concrete or steel sheet pilings that cover the bottom of a water body. Avoid solid docks, which can increase erosion. Any permanent dock will also require SRD approval.

Size

- In deciding size, consider how you will use the dock (e.g., boat mooring only or other activities such as sunning), safety factors (e.g., children passing each other), the style of dock, and regulations governing width.

> *When we bought our property, neighbours told me they'd been leaving their dock in the lake over the winter for years, with no problems. We decided to do the same, but during the spring melt, a strong south wind blew the ice towards the shore and buckled our dock.*
>
> Shoreline resident

Did you know . . . Unprotected polystyrene (EPS) foam is a poor choice for dock flotation. Unless it's completely encased, sun, gasoline and animals can cause it to break apart, littering the shoreline with bits of EPS foam.

Consider sharing a dock with a neighbour. Agree in writing how responsibilities for maintenance will be shared, and what will happen if either of your properties are sold.

Floating docks

Made of wood, fibre-glass, plastic or cement; tethered to the shore. Flotation is provided either by the wood used for the dock or by building buoyant material into it. Most floating docks are accessed from shore by a ramp which moves up and down with changing water levels. Consider adding a second rectangular section to make an 'L' or 'T' shape to provide more versatility and stability.

Floating Docks

advantages:

- Relatively easy to build; relatively economical.
- Adaptable to many types of shorelines.
- Distance between the top of the dock's deck and the surface of the water remains constant.
- Can be used in deep waters.
- Minimal direct disruption to submerged lands.
- Approval not usually required since dock will be pulled ashore in the fall.

disadvantages:

- Can lack stability; best if made long, wide, low and heavy (minimum size of 2 m x 6 m [6 ft x 20 ft] recommended).
- Blocks sunlight for aquatic plants and harms fish habitat.
- Heavy; pulling ashore can damage the banks of your shoreline.
- May not last as long as other docks as most of its surface is in constant contact with water.

Pipe docks

Structure commonly made of wood which sits above the water and is supported on thin pipe posts.

Specialty Docks

advantages:

- No disruption to water or water body floor.
- Can be used in shallow water.

disadvantages:

- Can be made out of wood but may need steel reinforcement if on a large body of water with heavy wave action.
- May be expensive to buy or build.
- May not be suitable for places with large changes in water levels.
- Requires approval from SRD.

Specialty docks

Other dock styles include cantilever docks, suspension docks and lift docks. A cantilever dock extends out over the water, supported by the header which is usually built entirely above the high water mark.

Pipe Docks

advantages:

- Generally the least costly dock option and easy to construct.
- Least environmental impact – minimal damage to submerged lands; sunlight can penetrate water below.
- Can be made narrow and small and still remain stable – good choice in shallow water.
- Will last longer than floating docks because less surface is in direct contact with water.
- Approval not usually required if removed in the fall.

disadvantages:

- Distance between dock surface and water surface will vary due to fluctuations in water levels; adjustable legs may be possible.
- Very sensitive to ice pressures; should be moved out of the water in the fall.
- Doesn't create a sheltered area for moorage.
- Maximum water depth 2 m (6 ft).

Did you know...

Permanent docks

Permanent docks are not usually approved in Alberta for private use on a public water body.

tip *A floating dock which you pull ashore during the winter does not usually need approval from SRD; however you may need approvals from the Navigable Waters officer at DFO.*

⚠️ **CAUTION**

Take care if you work with treated wood; it is very toxic:

- **Do any cutting well back from the water.**
- **Catch sawdust on a tarp.**
- **Let the finished structure cure and dry out before moving it into the water.**
- **Dispose of scraps in your local landfill. Do not burn.**

Building the Dock

Materials

- Choose non-toxic building materials whenever possible. Although costly, cedar, with its natural preservative, is an excellent material to use for decking. Douglas fir, because of its strength, is often used for structural support, although it rots more easily than cedar. Check whether the wood you have in mind will be approved before you proceed with your design. In some areas, wood treated with preservative (pressure-treated) may not be approved because the chemicals used may compromise water quality. Avoid pressure-treated wood for decking.

- There are many acceptable alternative materials and designs available for dock construction – for structural support, flotation, and decking. Check with suppliers and evaluate your options.

- If you choose to use concrete, purchase pre-cast concrete structures if possible. For building concrete supports in water, we recommend you hire a contractor. Until it fully hardens, concrete is very toxic to aquatic life. Concrete structures, however, are rarely approved by Fisheries and Oceans Canada (DFO).

- Do not use old railway ties as they leach toxic chemicals when submerged.

- Steel structures are generally not recommended for use in or near water. Where metal retaining walls extend below the average annual high-water mark, contact the local DFO office.

- Consider the new UV resistant plastics or fibreglass for decking, or cedar decking combined with plastic flotation.

- Use clean rocks taken from upland areas for any work on your dock; removing rocks from below the high water mark can expose your shoreline to erosion, and disturb shoreline habitat.

- Purchase quality hardware designed to resist corrosion – galvanized steel or stainless steel corner brackets, hinges, nuts, bolts and screws. The extra expense will be worth it in the extended life expectancy of your dock. Pay particular attention to the quality of coated screws and bolts used.

- Avoid using tires as boat bumpers on your dock unless you have cleaned them thoroughly with soap and water, away from the shoreline.

- Avoid recycling old materials such as steel drums and old car parts for shoreline construction projects.

Construction Guidelines

- Build your shoreline access first, and confine your traffic to that trail.

- Keep your trail as narrow as possible; if greater width is needed for construction purposes, make a temporary path which you can later allow to grow back with native ground cover. Keep ground cover low in the area where you will be pulling the dock out.

- Minimize the amount of shoreline vegetation that is removed for dock construction, to protect your shoreline from erosion.

Tips for Purchasers

If you are buying property with a dock make sure that approvals were obtained. Licences *do not* automatically transfer upon sale of the land. Make sure your offer to purchase makes clear that you will be asking SRD to transfer the licence to your name. If this is not done, the present owner may still have some rights to the dock.

If you are buying property without a dock and you wish to install one, check that the property is suitable. Look for things like exposure to winds, waves and moving ice, and whether your neighbours have docks. If they don't, this is a clue that your dock may not last.

- Time your construction activities to avoid fish spawning and when the young fry are active. DFO or SRD can advise you on timing windows for preventing harm to species in your area.
- If feasible, consider floating in some materials by boat to minimize damage.

More tips

- Avoid painting or staining your dock. Cedar will last a long time and weather beautifully without a finish. If you must paint:
  - Never apply wood preservatives or paint while docks are in or over the water.
  - Use a drop cloth or tarp for all sanding, painting and staining.
- If repainting or restaining, maintaining the same colour will minimize the amount of paint required.
- For more information on building near the water, refer to Chapter 4.

Legalities

In most cases, the land below high water belongs to the Crown. *See Chapter 17.* Because of this, all permanent dock structures require approval by one or more government agencies. In Alberta, the first contact for application to the Crown is Alberta Sustainable Resource Development. However, before you submit your application, check with your local municipality to identify any local regulations pertaining to docks.

The application process

To evaluate the potential impacts of your proposed dock structure, (as well as stairs or other elements), review officials will require detailed information. Seasonal docks do not usually require an approval but they are still subject to minimum standards. The sketch plan that you will have prepared for planning your dock and access route will be useful to assist in this.

You may be asked to provide information on your construction details; dock design, shoreline alterations (if required), materials, methods, time of construction. Agencies may also want to know about the area your dock will be located in, soil and vegetation types, distances to streams, and wildlife in the area. They will ask for colour photos, confirmation of property ownership, and may want you to talk about surrounding uses, other docks in the area, distances to property lines and neighbours' docks, and how your dock will affect neighbours' views.

As part of the approval process, your application will be sent to other agencies (such as DFO, Canadian Coast Guard and the local municipality). It may also be sent to First Nations groups and relevant interest groups. The approval process may include a site visit.

A dock design which is habitat-friendly and protects shorelines from erosion is much more likely to be approved. Do your research to make sure your proposal will satisfy the evaluation criteria, and you'll save time... and maybe even some money.

DFO is taking me to court! I hired a backhoe to excavate a channel for boat access for my grandchildren. The next thing I knew, a Fisheries officer showed up and told me I'd broken the law! I don't believe it, I've always considered myself a law-abiding citizen.

Shoreline resident

Resources

Guidelines for Lakeshore Use (pamphlet). Alberta Sustainable Resource Development and Alberta Environment.

Working Around Water Fact Sheets. Fisheries and Oceans Canada. (204) 983-5163 www.dfo-mpo.gc.ca/regions/CENTRAL/pub/fact-fait/fact-fait_e.htm

The Dock Manual. 1999. Burns, Max. Storey Books. North Adams, Massachusetts.

See Appendix 1 for complete Resources.

The small choices we make in daily living can have a big impact on the health of our shorelines.

Day-to-Day Living

10 H-E-A-L-T-H-Y Waterfront Living

Small Changes Add Up

*"**T**oo much work." It was a Saturday, and we had organized a crew of cleaners to ready our waterfront cottages for the next week's guests – scrub the kitchens and bathrooms, clean the windows, make the beds. Our head housekeeper was looking doubtfully at the baking soda and scrubbie we wanted her to use on all the sinks, and the diluted vinegar in a spray bottle for mirrors and windows. She was convinced that her crew would scrub their arms off and get poor results. But after the first sink was done using baking soda, she was a changed woman.*

In this chapter we look at some of the day to day things that we do around the house or the cottage, and provide tips and alternatives for H – E – A – L – T – H – Y waterfront living. Topics include:

H Home on the Water's Edge
E Environment-friendly Living
A Alternative Cleaning Products
L Lifestyles by the Water
• conserving water
• vehicles and equipment
• driveways and paths

T Tips for Outdoor Living
• friendly gardens
• instead of pesticides
• disposing of hot tub and pool water
• be light smart
• burn carefully
H Healthy Homes
• reduce your toxic load
• reduce, re-use, recycle
Y Your shoreline commitment

Home on the Water's Edge

Imagine that you have chosen to live in a boat for a year on a tiny freshwater lake. You use the lake's water for drinking and as a disposal site (you have nowhere else), so you don't want to pollute it with your wastes. Everything you do – washing the dishes, using the toilet, travelling about – could affect the safety and cleanliness of the water and your ability to survive. This is what it is like when we add the cumulative impacts of each person who lives on the land beside water.

Living beside water is like living in an "environmental risk zone". If we spill a dangerous household product, or wash one into our septic system, there is an increased risk that the ingredients in that product could find their way quickly, even directly, into our waters – either in surface run-off or through groundwater.

Because we are all in the same boat, the lifestyle choices we make affect our neighbours, just as our neighbours' choices affect us. Each individual and each household can make a difference – and it's in our interest!

> **tip** *Evaluate whether there are more effective and safer alternatives to the ways you have been doing things. Many products which we use regularly may have safer alternatives.*

Environment-friendly Living

Does "environment-friendly living" mean going back in time to the labour intensive days of 100 years ago? We believe that in the 21st century we can choose to be environment-friendly, without exhausting drudgery, by:

- Using common sense.
- Reducing what we waste.
- Finding alternatives.
- Making informed decisions when purchasing products for use in and around our homes.

For example, consider asking yourself what does "clean" really mean? If you have to use many toxic products to clean your house – is it really "clean" and healthy? Products that are safer for you are generally also better choices for protecting the environment. They may save you time and money too! Choose products which make clear specific claims such as "Phosphate-free". A general claim such as "natural" or "non-toxic" is vague and lacks specific references to scientific tests or ingredients.

Alternative Cleaning Products

Many household products that we use everyday to clean, polish, freshen and disinfect may be harmful. These range from toxic chemicals that are dangerous to inhale (in disinfectants, for example) to products which can burn skin and cause permanent eye damage (such as commercial drain cleaners).

Even if we have been careful when we use these products inside our homes, when we release them into the environment, we expose animals, plants, surface and groundwater – and eventually ourselves – to these chemicals.

Some cleaning products also contain high levels of phosphates which can promote algal blooms on surface water. Excess nitrates (from ammonia, for example) can also promote algae in watercourses.

There are alternatives which are better for our health and for the environment. Many cleaning challenges can be handled with the basic household products of our Safe Cleaning Kit .

You can also ask your grocery store to start carrying alternative cleaners, and give them a try! There are now some fairly well known brand names (including Canadian ones) which provide alternatives to toxic products. *Check the Resources section.*

Safe Cleaning Kit

These products provide safe cleaning power:
baking soda
vinegar
pure liquid soap
vegetable oil
washing soda
green scrubbie,
stiff brush, steel wool

Borax, hydrogen peroxide, and ammonia can also be used, but are more toxic and require caution. Wear rubber gloves and work only in a well ventilated area. Use ammonia sparingly!

Small changes...

Many of us find change difficult; try making small changes first. For example:

- **Reduce the quantity of cleaner or disinfectant that you use by diluting it with water in a spray bottle. Rather than spraying directly into the toilet or onto the counter, spray onto a rag.**
- **Cut down the amount of regular laundry detergent you use. Some researchers say that our clothes will be just as clean if we use only half what the manufacturers recommend on the label.**
- **Try something simple, like baking soda, a green scrubbie and just enough water to make a slightly damp paste. You'll be amazed – just as our house-keeper was – at how this will clean sinks, chrome, teapots, and cutlery.**

tip *Minimize the amount of detergents and cleaners you use. Even phosphate-free ones may contain additives to enhance cleaning power which can be just as harmful to water as phosphates.*

tip *Baking soda can be purchased in bulk quantities. Pure liquid soap is available at health food stores.*

"After years of using an automatic dishwasher, we've started hand-washing dishes again (parties excepted!). It's not much more work, we're avoiding those high phosphate detergents, saving energy and water – and best of all, we have some great conversations with the kids while we do the dishes."

Sarah and Clive

Some alternative cleaners:

All purpose cleaner
- Mix 125 ml (1/2 c) pure liquid soap with 4 L (l gal) of hot water. OR
- Dissolve 65 ml (4 Tbsp) of baking soda in 1 L (4 c) hot water. OR
- For an effective scouring cleaner, use baking soda as a dry powder with a slightly damp green scrubbie or dampened stiff brush.

Bleach for laundry
- Hydrogen peroxide bleaches. OR
- 125 ml (1/2 c) washing soda. OR
- 125 ml (1/2 c) borax.

Deodorizers
- Sprinkle baking soda on carpets and furniture, then vacuum. OR
- Mix a few drops of an essential oil like lemon, orange, peppermint, or lavender with water. These are available through health food stores. Use the mix in a diffuser or as a room spray to get the fresh smell of commercial air fresheners. OR
- Drops of essential oils can also be added to baking soda and used as above. OR
- Prevent the problem to start with – stop moisture from accumulating, have adequate ventilation, ensure your doors, windows and walls are sealed properly and repair any cracks or broken panes.

Detergent: laundry
- Use vegetable-based liquid detergents which use coconut oil to make suds. (Avoid detergents with phosphates, enzymes and /or bleach.) OR
- Add 65 ml (about 1/4 c) washing soda as the machine is filling. Put in clothes then add 375 ml (1 1/2 c) of pure soap flakes (not detergent). Add 65 ml (1/4 c) vinegar during first rinse.

Detergent: dish washing
- Very few automatic dishwasher detergents are available which contain no phosphates, bleach or enzymes. OR
- Hand wash with soap flakes dissolved in hot water. Add vinegar for tough grease.

Disinfectant
- Add 125 ml (1/2 c) borax to 4 L (1 gal) of hot water. OR
- Clean surfaces regularly with soap and hot water. Any disinfectant will only keep a surface bacteria-free for a short time, especially in a place like a toilet bowl.

Drain cleaner
- Almost all chemical drain cleaners are hazardous. Use a plunger or metal snake if your drain is blocked.
- Prevent the problem to start with; cover sinks, tubs and shower drains with screens or drain baskets to keep out food and hair. Never pour grease down drains. To keep drains clean, pour 125 ml (1/2 c) of baking soda down the drain and follow with 125 ml (1/2 c) vinegar. Let stand 15 minutes, then flush with hot water.

Furniture polish
- Check labels for those brands based on vegetable oils or non-toxic mineral oil. OR
- Dissolve 5 ml (1 tsp) lemon oil in 250 ml (l c) vegetable, linseed or mineral oil and apply with a clean dry rag. OR
- Apply olive oil directly.

Glass cleaner
- Add 65 ml (4 Tbsp) vinegar or 15 ml (1 Tbsp) lemon juice to a one litre (4 c) spray bottle of warm water.

Oven cleaner
- Place a deep pan of water in the oven, and turn oven on to a low temperature. Leave for two hours so that inside of oven is humid. This helps soften baked on grease. Mix a paste of equal parts baking soda and water and apply it with a stiff scrubbing pad to the walls of the oven, then rinse off.

Lifestyles by the Water

Conserving water

Sometimes, a few minor adjustments in your family's daily routine can have a large positive impact on your health, your pocketbook – and your shoreline. Water conservation provides a good example of this. **Conserving water doesn't mean doing without; it's about reducing what you waste.**

Conserving water means that you save energy and the dollars required to heat and pump water. You extend the life of your pump, water heater and your septic system – and that means less time and money spent on maintenance and replacement. For septic system users, water conservation is critical to the maintenance of the system.

Water reduction in a community can mean savings on infrastructure costs to upgrade and maintain water and sewage systems. These savings are then reflected in lower taxes. Conserving water also increases treatment plant efficiency, reduces the amount of chemicals needed to treat wastewater, and it protects water quality through improved wastewater treatment.

In the bathroom – toilets

- Replace your old 20 L (4.5 gal) per flush toilet with an efficient new 6 L (1.25 gal) per flush toilet. **This is the single most effective way to reduce the amount of water wasted in the bathroom** – you may reduce your indoor water use by 30%! Not all 6 L (1.25 gal) toilets perform equally well, even if they have CSA approvals. Before you buy, do your research and check out an independent study of 6 L (1.25 gal) toilets. *See Appendix 1.*

- As an alternative, place an insert filled with sand or water in your toilet tank. Use a clean, sealed plastic container or one purchased from a hardware store. Avoid using bricks; pieces of decaying brick can get under the rubber flapper and cause leaks. After installation, check that the toilet still provides a complete flush. With older tanks, less volume may mean an incomplete flush and having to flush twice – which defeats your purpose!

In the bathroom – tubs, showers and sinks

- Install a low flow showerhead; new designs now provide plenty of spray.
- Instead of letting the tap run...
  - Fill the basin with water when you shave or wash.
  - Use short bursts of water when brushing your teeth.

In the kitchen

- Fix leaky faucets right away. It's often a washer that needs replacing, a fairly quick and easy repair.
- Screw an aerator to your faucet to reduce your water use at the sink by 25%.
- Instead of letting the tap run...
  - Keep a pitcher of water in the fridge for cold drinks.
  - Clean produce in a partially filled sink or bowl.
  - Take foods out of the freezer in advance to thaw in the fridge.
  - When hand-washing dishes, put soapy water in one sink and rinse water in the other (or a basin).

In the utility room

- When using your washing machine, adjust the amount of water according to size of the load; if possible, wait until you have full loads of laundry.
- Insulate your electric hot water heater and lower the thermostat to save on heating costs.
- Insulate the hot water pipes (with pipe wrap) to avoid having to let the tap run as long to get hot water.
- If your water softener backwash line is connected to your septic system, recharge your softener as infrequently as possible to avoid overloading your septic system. Some models recharge only after a certain amount of water passes through the system, rather than at timed intervals. These are preferable because you will save on softener salts, and use less water.

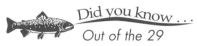

Did you know ... Out of the 29 OECD countries, Canada ranks second highest in water consumption per capita. Many Europeans get by on a quarter of what we use.

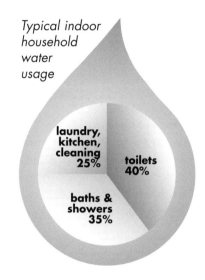

Typical indoor household water usage

laundry, kitchen, cleaning **25%**

toilets **40%**

baths & showers **35%**

tip *Check your toilet for leaks. Put one or two drops of food colouring in your tank; if it seeps into your toilet bowl, the rubber flapper is ready for replacement.*

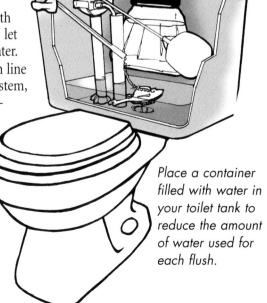

Place a container filled with water in your toilet tank to reduce the amount of water used for each flush.

To reduce pollution, consider upgrading equipment like lawnmowers and weed trimmers to products which meet EPA 2006 (or better) standards.

⚠ **CAUTION**

Avoid sodium chloride salt and urea (a fertilizer sold as a de-icer) to de-ice sidewalks and stairs. Both are tough on plants and surface water.

Vehicles and equipment

- Store all fuels safely, and well away from surface water or wells.
- Periodically check fuel storage tanks, valves and hoses for leaks.
- When adding oil or fuel:
  - Work over a hard surface like concrete.
  - Use drop cloths.
  - Always use a funnel to limit spills.
  - Wrap a rag around the intake.
  - Go slowly and listen for the sound of changing air pressure as you reach tank capacity.
- Put together a Green Clean-up Bin for spills or leaks, and always have it on hand. *See Chapter 4 for details.*
- Be careful when adding ethylene glycol-based antifreeze since it is highly toxic. Look for the much less toxic propylene glycol-based antifreeze.
- Keep your vehicles well maintained. Use the absorbent material from your Green Clean-up Bin to blot up any leak of oil, transmission fluid or antifreeze.

- Wash your vehicle at a commercial car wash, where soapy water is recycled. If a car wash is unavailable, pull your car onto grass and wash it there using a hose with a trigger nozzle and a phosphate-free detergent. If you wash it in the street or your driveway, suds can run down the gutter and into surface water.

Driveways and paths

- Sweep your driveway and sidewalk instead of washing them down with a hose, to prevent sediment, salt and petroleum products from washing into storm sewers or drainage ditches.
- Avoid using oil on a dusty driveway; runoff from the next rainfall will carry some of the oil with it.
- For icy surfaces, use inexpensive sand, grit (such as limestone), sawdust or cinders. It only takes a thin layer of any of these products, scattered down the wheel track of your drive or along your walkway, to provide traction. Environment-friendly de-icers are also available at hardware stores.

Tips for Outdoor Living

It's easy, when we're outdoors, to feel small in comparison to the vastness of water, forests, earth and sky. We tend to think that the wide world out there is too big to be affected by what we do in our own little corner. The fact is, though, that how we garden, or what we do with our pool water, can make a difference.

Friendly gardens

With surface water so close, it is extra important to carefully manage your vegetable garden. There are now great resources available to help you garden in ways that conserve water, encourage beneficial insects and use non- or low-chemical fertilizers and pesticides.

Choose a suitable location

- Ideally, put your garden in a sunny, level or slightly sloping spot with good drainage.

- Keep your garden away from the shoreline; as part of a wildlife corridor, it may end up hosting many extra guests for dinner!
- If you have to garden on a slope:
  - Avoid slopes and drainage channels which let topsoil and soil additions wash away during heavy rains.
  - Avoid planting your garden on, or uphill from, your septic drainfield or mound. Watering your garden could cause your system to become saturated.

Water wisely

- If possible, install a drip irrigation or soaker hose system; it allows water to seep slowly into the ground, reducing evaporation and preventing runoff.
- When using a sprinkler system, water only as needed to encourage deep root growth, and slowly, to prevent runoff.
- Invest in a timer to prevent overwatering.

Collect rainwater in barrels or a cistern and use it to water your garden.

- Use a rain gauge or tin can to measure rainfall and irrigation quantities. A total of 2.5 cm (1 in) per week is usually adequate.

Use mulch

- Use a thick layer of a mulch like straw or shredded leaves to conserve water.

Use compost

Compost is a good alternative to chemical fertilizer; it feeds your soil, and enhances its structure and organic content. Composting helps divert materials from landfills, reducing garbage disposal costs for your family.

- Keep compost piles well back from the water's edge, drainageways, and out of the way of any obvious animal paths.
- Make sure that any moisture seeping from the pile does not get to the shoreline where it could harm your water quality.

Instead of pesticides...

⚠️ **CAUTION: The next time you are tempted to use a pesticide, first consider alternatives.**

Pesticides are chemical substances that are designed to destroy insects and weeds. More and more research indicates that they can also harm people and animals. Young children, because of their small size and under-developed immune systems, are especially at risk. Pests can develop a tolerance for chemicals used to control them. Inappropriate use of pesticides can pollute our water.

Beating the bugs

While pesticides are intended to combat problem insects in the garden, they also can damage the beneficial insects and birds which prey on the pests. There are many other ways to deal with bugs that have stood the test of generations of gardeners and farmers.

Your most effective defence is to provide the best possible growing conditions to maximize the health of your plants. Stressed plants are more susceptible to pests and diseases.

- Mix your crops and interplant with herbs and companion plants. Plants such as marigolds, onions, garlic and herbs keep bugs away, so plant a row in with your vegetables. Avoid planting large areas with just one type of crop. Such areas are more vulnerable to insect damage.

- Practise crop rotation – plant the same crop in different areas of your garden each year. Follow leaf vegetables or "heavy feeders" like tomatoes with nitrogen providing legumes such as peas and beans.
- Water in the morning rather than at night, to avoid creating the moist environment that some insects and diseases thrive in.
- Cultivate natural predators. Ladybugs, garter snakes, bats, toads, and birds eat insect pests. Encourage insect-eating birds in your yard by creating bird-friendly habitat. *See Chapters 7 and 11.*
- Use barrier methods such as floating row covers, cutworm collars, or bands of diatomaceous earth.
- Use manual methods. Remove eggs, larvae, cocoons, and adults from plants by hand or dislodge pests by spraying water.
- If you are sure the insect is harmful, use soap-based products which will kill the insects without harming you or leaving a toxic residue behind.

Out with weeds

- Mulching is one of the best ways to prevent weeds. While your seeds are sprouting, hand weed small gardens and raised beds. Then, once your seedlings are strong and tall enough, weed again and apply a thick layer of mulch.
- If you pull weeds regularly when they are small, you'll have fewer weeds later in the growing season and the following year.
- Consider using a weed barrier cloth for really difficult areas.
- *See the section in Chapter 7 on alien invaders for more weed control tips.*

⚠️ **CAUTION: If you do use pesticides:**

- Read and follow directions very carefully, and apply only in the ratio prescribed and to the particular plants or areas you are targeting. Applying more chemicals than directed may do more harm than good.

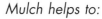

Mulch helps to:
- *Keep weeds and insects out of your garden.*
- *Hold water in the soil.*
- *Protect plant roots from excessive heat or cold.*
- *Increase yields (earlier blossoming and harvesting).*
- *Reduce splashing (keeps your vegetables clean).*
- *Increase fertility and improve soil structure.*
- *Reduce erosion from water and wind.*

Did you know . . .
On average, one-third of our household waste can be composted, and during the growing season, as much as three-quarters!

 CAUTION

Pesticides can kill insects which help your garden, like ground beetles, ladybug beetles, lacewings, wasps, and spiders.

Did you know . . .

Studies show that plants grown in compost are more resistant to disease than those grown with chemical fertilizers.

⚠ CAUTION

Never drain treated pool water where it will run off or seep into nearby water bodies. Chemicals like chlorine are toxic to fish and wildlife, and differences in alkalinity between pool water and surface water can harm fish and wildlife.

Did you know . . .

The yellow fish painted on roads beside storm drains is a reminder that everything which goes down the gutter eventually ends up in surface water – and fish habitat.

tip *Cover your winter sand supply to keep moisture out, prevent it from freezing, and stop it from eroding. Insulate the pile with fibreglass insulation, double bagged in plastic, and tied between the two halves of a folded tarp. You may not need to add salt to the sand.*

- Never spray near wells or surface water (including ditches and canals).
- Spray on windless days to avoid drift.
- Do not spray on days when rain is forecast, and wait at least a day before you irrigate.
- Never use pesticides on eroded areas; rain may wash them off to surface water.
- Always keep children and pets off areas that have been treated with pesticides.

Disposing of hot tub and pool water

If you have a pool or hot tub, take precautions to prevent damage to surface water.

Treating your water

While chlorine is the least expensive option, it is hard on your skin, and has significant environmental impacts.

- Consider using bromine instead of chlorine to treat pool water, especially hot tubs. However, bromine may not be suitable for pools or hot tubs exposed to the sun.
- Check with your supplier about UV and ozone treatments.

Emptying a pool or hot tub

- Remove the chlorine or bromine dispenser several days prior to emptying the water. Stop using your pool after removal.
- If you live within a municipality with a sanitary sewer system, empty the water into the sewer line (not the storm drain). Treated water that goes into storm drains makes its way into surface water.
- If you're outside a municipality with a sewer system, empty the pool into a dry well or pump the water out and spray it over a large, vegetated area, well away from drainageways and water bodies. Do not empty it into your septic tank – you can overload the system.

Be light smart

In dark rural areas, outside lighting is a necessity. Yet, even one outdoor light can be very intrusive to your neighbours – and can spoil the peaceful, rustic atmosphere of your shoreline setting. Poor outdoor lighting can also send enough light into the sky to interfere with stargazing for quite a distance. Choose and install your lighting carefully.

- Wherever possible, place light high and directed down towards the areas you need lit, rather than towards the sky and open areas.
- Use low intensity halogen lights, or lights on dimmer switches, to reduce harshness. You can also use yellow "bug" lamps for softer porch lighting, but they use more electricity and are more costly.
- Avoid bright "dawn-to-dusk" mercury vapour yard lamps. They are expensive to operate, produce harsh glare, and waste almost 30% of the light they emit.
- Use motion sensor lights (with amber floodlights) to avoid having lights on all the time. They will also save you money!

Burn carefully

Smoke particles can cause health problems for you, your family, your neighbours, and wildlife. Ash entering freshwater systems can have a significant negative impact on water quality and wildlife health as it may carry contaminants into the water. Burning beach wood may deprive your shoreline of its protective armour.

- Keep burning to a minimum. If you burn during the day, smoke will generally blow from the water to the land; in the evening, smoke will generally drift out towards the water with the "evening downdraft".
- Avoid lighting fires during air inversions; since surface water is frequently located in low spots, smoke and other pollutants may be trapped near the ground.
- If you are considering burning waste:
  - Compost or recycle wood and paper, instead of burning. Do not burn toxic materials such as plastic, rubber, oil, asphalt shingles, and treated wood.
  - Contact your municipality for information on your recycling and hazardous materials disposal options, and for burning regulations that apply to your area. You may need a burning permit.
- If you are burning for home heating:
  - Buy an efficient, certified woodstove that's the right size for your needs, and make sure that it's installed correctly.
  - Burn only wood that has been properly seasoned for at least six months.

Healthy Homes

Reduce your toxic load

Consider alternatives to some of the other toxic materials which may be in your home.

Paints

- Acrylic and latex paints are water-based and less toxic than oil-based paints. Favour paints containing ethyl or iso-propyl alcohol, acetone, or odourless mineral spirits.
- There are now water-based paints on the market made with "natural" ingredients that use few, if any volatile solvents. Many major paint manufacturers also make low-odour and less toxic paints as well.

Thinners and strippers

- Non-chlorinated solvents (rubbing alcohol, grain alcohol, nail polish remover and turpentine) are less toxic than their chlorinated counterparts such as paint thinner.
- Eliminate the need for thinners by buying water-based paint. Take paint off your skin with margarine or baby oil. Avoid paint strippers by heat-stripping, sanding or using new "safe stripper" products.

Wood preservatives

- Copper or zinc naphthenate and copper-8 quinolinolate are the least acutely toxic wood preservatives. However copper and zinc preservatives are not effective on wood which comes into contact with soil.
- Use naturally weather resistant wood such as cedar for picnic tables, decks and fences, and protect with a water repellent paint or linseed oil.
- Use pressure treated wood only for structural support and only when there's no alternative. Never use it for children's play structures. *See sidebar Pg 82.*

Buying, storing and disposing of toxic products

Evaluate your need before purchasing toxic products. Are there alternatives? Make sure the product will do what you want it to, and buy only the amount that you will use.

- Dispose of toxic products at hazardous products collection depots, not with your regular household waste. Never pour leftovers down your drain, on the ground, or into storm sewers.
- Don't store paints or pesticides where they can freeze. Once they thaw out, they are unusable and simply pose a problem for disposal.
- Check with your municipality about local facilities for disposing of batteries, used oil, paint, pesticides, and solvents.

Reduce, reuse, recycle

Disposing of garbage at landfills costs money; and many garbage pick-up services are now charging a fee per bag of garbage taken away, so it is in your best interest to REDUCE the amount of garbage you produce. You can cut your garbage bills by composting, RECYCLING what you can, and RE-USING materials for other purposes.

- Check with your local municipality to find out what materials are accepted by recycling centres in your area.
- Set a covered compost collection pail in a handy location in your kitchen and empty regularly to prevent odours and flies.
- Set up an accessible area with labeled recycling boxes so you can "sort as you go".
- Check local resources to find out who will take items you no longer need.

> *I've got a cupboard full of toxic products I never use down in the basement. I just don't know how to get rid of them.*
>
> Shoreline resident

Did you know . . . There are no safe disposal methods for many hazardous products. Since they must not go down the sink or into your garbage, the best solution is not to purchase them in the first place.

Did you know . . . Residential use of pesticides, per acre, is more intensive than on most farms.

tip The B.C. Organic Growers' Standards Guide suggests several alternatives to pressure-treated wood: concrete, steel, galvanized metal, charred cedar, and charred pine.

Your Shoreline Commitment

Making a difference often starts with a few small changes. Try some of the suggestions in this book, and review how you're doing a few months later.

With your HEALTHY waterfront lifestyle, consider completing the Shoreline Action Checklist at the back of this book. Mail it to us at The Living by Water Project, or go online to our website at www.livingbywater.ca. You'll be joining other shoreline residents across Canada who are helping to protect and restore shorelines!

Resources

See Appendix 1 for complete Resources.

11 Living With Wildlife

Awesome or Awful?

"We have bed bugs – green creepy-crawlies between the sheets." The young couple had booked a weekend romantic getaway and were standing, distressed, in our office. Sure enough, when we inspected the bed, there were the offending critters – not bed bugs, but definitely between the sheets. It was our first season, and after apologetically giving the couple a refund, we called in a fumigator who dealt with the "problem" chemically. Of course, we then found the real problem: a torn window screen, a branch too close to the building, and a tree covered with caterpillars. That was the last time we used chemicals against the wildlife whose home we shared. We became wiser with experience and put our effort instead into preventing such unwanted encounters.

Watching the birds and other life that abounds on the water's edge is one of the many "perks" of shoreline living. But we generally prefer that the wild creatures stay outside of our home! Mice in our pantry, bears in our garbage, or bugs in our beds are all scenarios we would prefer to avoid. This chapter gives tips for living in neighbourly ways with the animals that share your property. If you can avoid having to deal with wildlife after they've become a problem, you'll save time and energy, and enjoy their presence more.

While we don't want wildlife in our homes, helping wildlife by protecting their homes makes sense. We have included some general tips in this chapter, and there are some project ideas in Chapter 7. And because our pets sometimes have encounters with wildlife, we have included suggestions for minimizing pet – wildlife conflict.

Keeping Wildlife Out of Your Home

Since it's their home we're sharing, we need to take the first steps to avoid negative encounters with wildlife. By wildlife-proofing our homes we can avoid unpleasant jobs like trapping or killing them with toxic substances when they get inside. **The most effective way to get rid of unwanted wildlife is prevention – keep them out of your home.**

General tips

Block access

Block all means of entry for insects, rodents and bats via foundations, porches and steps; through doors and windows; through holes in roofs or eaves; through cracks in floors, ceilings, and walls; and through access points for wires and pipes. *See also Pg 22.*

- Seal with caulk, weather-stripping, expandable foam, crumpled heavy-duty aluminum foil, metal flashing and/or steel wool.
- Use fine wire mesh screens on all doors, opening windows and vents, including attic and underfloor vents.

Discourage contact

- Trim tree limbs that touch your roof or the walls of your home or outbuildings.
- Store firewood and lumber away from main buildings, or in a special shelter.
- Use yellow light bulbs in all outside light fixtures to reduce the numbers of flying insects attracted to the house at night.

Keep food away

- Use animal-proof garbage cans, and if feasible, keep garbage cans in a shed or garage until garbage can be removed. If there are bears in your area, and you can't safely store your garbage indoors, construct a very sturdy container and remove your garbage often.
- Keep pet food inside to avoid attracting wildlife. If you must feed pets outdoors, remove any food dishes and leftover food after feeding.

- If you have fruit trees or berry bushes, harvest the fruit (including windfalls) to discourage bears. Pick fruit early and don't allow fallen fruit to accumulate on the ground. Consider fencing your garden area.
- Maintain your compost; turn it regularly and cover with dirt or leaves. Improperly maintained compost piles and bins can attract many animals, including bears, skunks, and raccoons.

  ⚠ **CAUTION:** ***Do not put meat or bones, dairy products, fats, plate scrapings or cooked grains in your compost.***

- Keep barbecue equipment clean and store your barbecue in a secure area. Bears are attracted to the rich odours.
- Prevent bird feed from accumulating on the ground to keep rodents and bears away, and avoid using suet in feeders; this can attract bears. Better yet, fill feeders only when bears are in hibernation. When bears are active, there are plenty of natural food sources for the birds.
- Keep all food (including pet food) in sturdy rodent- and insect-proof containers. Remember, mice can chew through some plastics!

Did you know . . .

The biggest problem facing wildlife today is "homelessness" (habitat loss and destruction). You can help keep wildlife out of your home by providing them with homes of their own.

⚠ **CAUTION**

A fed bear is a dead bear! **Bears and other predators that have regular access to human garbage become dangerous to humans and must often be killed.**

Store garbage, bird seed, barbecues and anything else attractive to bears and raccoons in a secure shed.

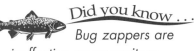

- Rinse out all recyclable containers (such as glass and plastic bottles, tins, cans and tetrapaks) and return them to the depot as soon as possible.
- Keep fruit bowls in the refrigerator in summer.
- Wash off garden vegetables, except potatoes and carrots, before storing them in the house or basement.

Clean regularly

- Wipe kitchen counters, stove tops and floors frequently.
- Keep drains clean and free of food scraps.
- Clean the kitchen fan regularly.
- Keep garbage cans tightly covered and wash them regularly.

Check building details

- Ensure house foundations are made of concrete or masonry. *See sidebar Chapter 9 for recommendations on use of treated wood.*
- Keep wood posts, beams, stair stringers and siding out of contact with the ground unless protected from decay.
- Make sure basements and crawl spaces are dry and well-ventilated.

Tips for specific wildlife
Insects

The presence of many kinds of insects along your shoreline is an indication that it is healthy. In our gardens, most insects are busy doing things that benefit us. They pollinate our gardens, help break down our compost, serve as food for birds and other wildlife, or attack and eat the insects that damage our crops. Encourage natural habitat, and you'll gain these insects as helpers! Try growing your garden without using pesticides; you'll keep chemicals out of our food chain, and avoid poisoning beneficial insects, birds and other wildlife which consume insects. *See Chapter 10 for tips on Beating the Bugs.*

⚠️ **CAUTION:** *If you find you have insects in your home, make sure that you know what they are before you act.* Many insects are harmless or even beneficial as they feed on other, more problematic insects. That said, here are some of the familiar "irritants" of the insect world, and what you can do to protect yourself from them.

Ants

If you find ants are entering your home, it is usually because they have found a food source.
- Thoroughly clean the area, and remove things like pop and beer cans. They will usually leave if they can't find any more food in your home.
- Seal all points of entry.
- Spread diatomaceous earth in a line along their point of entry to keep ants out. Diatomaceous earth also works on earwigs and silverfish. Other substances which may help deter ants include red chili powder, paprika, or dried peppermint leaves or a few drops of peppermint, lavender, lemongrass or cedarwood essential oils.
- Carpenter ants (the largest of our common ants) are beneficial insects in their natural environment. If you find particles resembling sawdust in your home, however, you might have an active nest of carpenter ants chewing on some damp wood somewhere.
  - Set bait made of sugar water and boric acid (a mild toxin of little threat to humans) over a period of weeks. Worker ants will take it back to feed the young ants and the queen, and the colony will be killed.

Mosquitoes

To minimize mosquito populations:
- Encourage insect-eating predators like dragonflies, bats, and birds (like swallows). *See suggestions in Chapter 7.*
- Get rid of old tires or store them under a shelter. Tires fill up with rainwater and make breeding pools for mosquitoes.
- Keep water-catching debris (sacks, pots etc.) out of your vegetable garden and try to eliminate pools of standing water in ditches and gutters.
- To keep mosquitoes away from your deck, try burning citronella candles or placing potted basil, lavender or citronella plants in outside recreational areas.

Wasps

Wasps are part of nature's "cleaning service", but they can be very annoying if you are trying to enjoy a barbecue on your deck.

- Make a wasp trap by slicing off the top quarter of a plastic pop bottle, inverting that section and taping it to the bottom part to create a funnel; then put an inch or two of juice or beer in the bottom. Leave the bottle near your outside eating area, and watch the wasps go for the fermenting liquid. They can easily get in – but will be trapped inside! Commercial versions are available.
- Avoid using spray "bombs" to kill wasp nests. Unless the wasp nest is outside your door, consider leaving it be. You can also try a pesticide-free approach; carefully remove the nest when the wasps are sluggish – late at night or early in the morning – and quickly drop it hole first into a large pail of water. Make sure you cover the pail! This job is easier with a second person; take extra care and wear protective clothing.

Birds

- Keep birds from colliding with window panes by hanging streamers or strings of fishing line in front of problematic areas or by attaching silhouettes of birds of prey like owls or hawks to the window glass. Commercial products are available.
- Keep wood siding well painted or stained to prevent insect infestations which attract woodpeckers. Stain the backside of new siding, and give extra treatment to any questionable areas. If woodpeckers still pick at your home's wood siding, try hanging a few lightweight aluminum foil plates along the areas they like best.
- If Canada geese have found your lawn and you would like them to move on:
  - Leave or plant a thick buffer of vegetation along the shoreline or streamside – geese don't like walking through tall plants.
  - Consider alternatives for your lawn such as a native groundcover – geese love lawn grass, especially rich fertilized grass!

Rodents

If you have squirrels, mice or voles in your house:

- Spray mice droppings with a 10% solution of bleach and water before cleaning up, to reduce the risk of contracting the dangerous hanta virus infection carried by some mice. Keep the bleach spray off clothing!
- Bait mouse traps with cheese or peanut butter. You may need to bait the traps for several days before actually setting them.
- Check traps regularly. Handle traps and carcasses with rubber gloves and disinfect in bleach solution.
- You may be able to find live traps for animals like squirrels or mice. They are usually available from the SPCA or a local farm supply centre, but watch the design. Some live traps are less humane than "spring" traps that kill quickly. Before trapping a squirrel, be sure that you don't have a nest of babies somewhere inside.

Bats

Encourage insect-eating bats to live on your property, by protecting native vegetation and installing a bat house. You'll benefit from their healthy appetite for a variety of insects – including mosquitoes.

- To reduce the chance of a bat inadvertently flying into your house, screen all windows and doors, as well as the chimney and vents. Seal soffits as for insects.

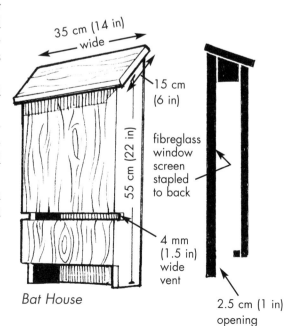

35 cm (14 in) wide

15 cm (6 in)

55 cm (22 in)

fibreglass window screen stapled to back

4 mm (1.5 in) wide vent

2.5 cm (1 in) opening

Bat House

❝ I've tried all different methods for keeping geese off my grass. Now I realize that the best idea is to reduce the size of my lawn. ❞

Shoreline resident

Did you know …
Canada geese are protected by the International Migratory Bird Convention Act; it is illegal to harm them or their eggs without a permit or a hunting licence.

⚠ **CAUTION**

DON'T handle bats! A small percentage of bats carry rabies, which can be transmitted through bites. Unusual behaviour (like flying during the day) may be a sign of rabies.

Locate a bat house at least 3-5 m (10-16 ft) above the ground, with a south or southeastern exposure that receives at least 4-6 hours of sunlight a day. In cool areas, paint the box a dark colour to increase the solar heat absorbed by the box.

tip *SKUNK DEODORIZER: To deodorize a dog that has had a run-in with a skunk, mix 500 ml (2 cups) hydrogen peroxide, 30 ml (2 tbsp) baking soda, and 5 ml (1 tsp) liquid hand soap and wash down the dog. (This may bleach the dog's fur.)*

Did you know ...

In some mountain parks, animal control officers successfully use aggressive body postures, sounds and tools such as rubber bullets and pyrotechnics to scare bears, teaching them to avoid human encounters.

Even small holes in the foundation or eaves of your house can invite unwelcome guests into your home.

- If a bat does accidentally get into your house, stay calm. Open all your doors and windows, and turn off the lights. The bat will quickly leave on its own.

To remove bats from your attic, the only safe and effective way is to lock them out. Wait until after June or July when the young are old enough to fly, so they are not trapped inside to starve.

- Find their exit holes: watch at dusk to see where bats emerge from the house, or look for droppings along the side of the house. A bat can squeeze through a hole the size of your thumb.
- Create a one-way escape valve by attaching a 30 cm (12 in) flap of fibreglass fly screen over the exit hole. The bats can fly out, but won't be able to get back in.
- Leave the screen in place for a few nights to make sure all the bats get out, then seal the holes permanently.

Skunks

Follow the tips at the beginning of this chapter; pay attention to low decks and keep pet access doors locked at nights and when not in use.

- Slotted metal vent covers are preferable to screen wire to keep skunks from entering your house through foundation vents.
- To seal a low backyard deck, use 6 mm (1/4 in) grid screening or solid metal flashing. Trench around the perimeter of the deck a minimum of 30 cm (12 in) deep, insert the screening in your trench and backfill. Attach the top of your screening to the face of your decking or its support beam with nails or fence post staples.

- To deodorize an area affected by a skunk, maximize ventilation, and place cotton balls saturated with a few drops of an essential oil like wintergreen, or sprinkle the area with baking soda.

Bears

Once a bear becomes accustomed to eating food from human settlements, it will be very reluctant to give up this easy access to a free lunch. Prevent bears from becoming a problem by following the steps outlined at the beginning of this chapter, especially those relating to food storage.

Beavers

Beavers play an important role in creating wetlands, but they can also damage trees and shrubs and alter watercourses. Trying to remove a beaver can prove to be a tough job; you may need to learn to coexist with them!

- You can protect trees from gnawing beavers by wrapping the tree in wire mesh. (Check mesh yearly to avoid tree damage.)

⚠ *CAUTION: If you feel that removing a beaver dam is absolutely necessary, consult with your local Alberta Fish and Wildlife office before acting.* Removing a dam may kill fish and other animals by draining upstream ponds and destroying important habitat. The change in water flow may also affect other downstream landowners in your area.

Animals in the garden

There are probably as many tips to prevent animals raiding your garden as there are gardeners; here are a few. *See also Chapter 10.*

- Hang mesh bags of human hair in ornamental shrubs to deter deer from grazing on new spring growth.
- Provide alternative food for rabbits such as Dutch white clover in the lawn mix to attract them away from the garden veggies. (Clover also acts as a natural fertilizer for your lawn, and makes a good alternative ground cover to turf grass.)
- Make your garden less appealing to bears, deer and raccoons, with a tall wire mesh fence or a low voltage electric fence. Apply peanut butter to the electric wires – bears will take a lick and learn a quick lesson.

Helping Wildlife in Their Homes

Less work for you helps wildlife

If you enjoy seeing wildlife on your waterfront, plan to protect their homes by leaving as much varied, natural plant cover as possible. This provides protection, shelter, and a variety of food sources. The less work you do in changing the original native vegetation on your property, the more wildlife will be attracted to your property!

By protecting habitat for wildlife, you'll gain in lots of ways. You'll be supporting the reestablishment of fish stocks in your area, or helping with their protection. You'll be encouraging natural predators of garden pests, making gardening more enjoyable. By encouraging habitat for insects, amphibians and fish, you'll be supporting the food needs of larger wildlife, like herons, loons, and eagles, which many of us (including children) enjoy watching and learning about.

You may wish to learn more about specific habitat needs of wildlife in your area, including species at risk. You may also wish to encourage particular kinds of wildlife or you may be living near a species that is particularly sensitive to human activity. *See Appendix 3 for information on living with sensitive wildlife and check Appendix 1 for help in all these areas.*

Shoreline landscaping

Follow the habitat and landscaping suggestions in Chapter 7 to protect or restore native vegetation and create your shoreline buffer.

- Leave rocks, logs, upland and aquatic vegetation to provide a variety of habitats.
- Leave a variety of landscape features on your property, to encourage a diversity of wildlife – native meadows for butterflies, dead snags for cavity nesting birds, rock piles or wild areas near fences for small mammals and garter snakes.

Habitat in urban areas

If you live in an urban area, consider providing even a small space for wildlife. A 2 m by 2 m (6 x 6 ft) area of shrubs and wildflowers can help provide habitat for birds and butterflies. There are many good sources of 'backyard habitat' projects. *See Appendix 1.* When combined with contributions by your neighbours, you can gradually build urban habitat.

- Choose native species *(Appendix 2)* which are helpful for wildlife. Select those that add style and colour to your landscape if you wish a landscaped look.
- Place a small sign to explain your "natural" area, such as "Butterfly Garden" or "Natural Area Being Restored". This will help your neighbours understand why you're choosing to park the mower!
- Butterflies love sunlight. Plant flowers that are rich in nectar in a sunny spot; hummingbirds' favourites are flowers that are red and trumpet-shaped.

Bird feeders

- Be rigorous about maintaining feeders, especially in winter months when birds may come to rely on the food source. Keep them clean to avoid transmitting disease within bird populations.
- Put a hummingbird feeder in a shady spot and fill it with a 1:4 mixture of sugar and water that has been boiled for about 4 minutes. Clean the feeder a minimum of every 3 days (more often in hot weather) to prevent the growth of dangerous mould.

In your garden

- Help wildlife by postponing fall clean-up until spring. Leave the plants in your flowerbeds over winter; seeds produced by some flowering plants provide food for seed-eating birds during the fall, winter and spring.
- Use leaves to mulch plants; they help some beneficial insects survive the winter.
- Maintain a compost pile to provide habitat for insects which help to decompose your compost, and increase foraging opportunities for insect-eating birds.

Wetlands

- Protect aquatic vegetation and wetland areas on your property. These areas are valuable for a wide variety of birds and other species. For further information, contact Ducks Unlimited. *See Appendix 1.*

Invasive species

- Help protect your water body from the introduction of invasive species which can compete with native wildlife.
- Never dump aquarium fish or turtles into a natural body of water. Most are not

Put up a sign to let the neighbours know why you're allowing an area to go wild.

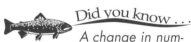

 Did you know ... A change in numbers and types of fish in the water may be a sign of a decline in the quality of fish habitat.

⚠ **CAUTION**
Leave wild fish in the wild. They are not adapted to aquarium life and will likely die. Removal decreases native fish stocks – and is illegal!

tip *If you find a dead animal that has been tagged, contact the Canadian Wildlife Service before disposing of it. See Resources.*

If someone's pet is chasing wildlife on your property, notify the owner. If the problem continues, contact your local animal control officer. You could be charged with theft for capturing and releasing the problem pet elsewhere.

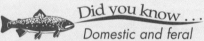

Did you know . . .

Under the Alberta Wildlife Act, a Conservation Officer can charge a pet owner and even capture or destroy a pet that is harassing wildlife.

Did you know . . .

Domestic and feral cats (wild descendants of abandoned pets) are responsible for killing one billion wild birds a year in North America. A cat can still kill when belled and declawed.

Did you know . . .

It is illegal to keep any wild animal for longer than 24 hours.

Resources

See Appendix 1 for complete Resources.

Make a cool, dark home for toads by placing an old 20 cm (8 in) clay pot upside down in a shady, moist, sheltered spot. Break a small hole in the side for an entrance, and these insect eaters will move in!

native to the area and will likely die. Those that do survive (such as goldfish) can threaten native species and ecosystems.

- *Review Chapter 14 for tips on boating to prevent the spread of invasive plants and animals via the water.*

Nest boxes and homes

Besides the bird houses mentioned in Chapter 7, consider nest boxes for ducks, osprey platforms, a bat house, or even a toad home. *See sidebars on this page and page 97. See Appendix 1 for further plans for bat houses, nest boxes for ducks, and other bird house plans.*

CAUTION: Take extra care in driving during times when wildlife is on the move. In many areas rich in shoreline habitat, you may encounter massive shorebird migrations, salamanders looking for ponds in the spring, or toads and snakes returning from winter hibernation.

Other wildlife challenges

Finding a dead animal

Living by water puts you in close contact with the circle of life.

- As a general rule, leave dead fish and other aquatic wildlife in place. As they decay, they return nutrients to the water. If you feel you must move the carcass out of the water, use a shovel to move the animal and bury it upland.
  - You will have to deal with the carcass yourself if you find a dead animal like a deer or bear on your property.

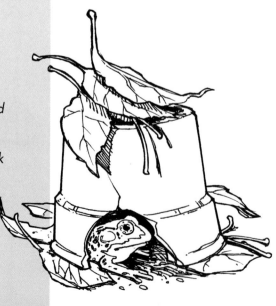

Orphaned and injured wildlife

Finding an injured animal, or an animal that appears to be abandoned, rouses our instincts to rescue and protect. It is often best to leave it alone; remember, its natural predators need to eat too! Also, beware of assuming that a young animal is abandoned. Animals rarely abandon their young; a young animal that appears to be abandoned usually has a parent(s) nearby. Before intervening, phone your local Conservation Officer or a nearby licenced wildlife centre for instructions on how to proceed.

CAUTION: Before attempting any action, make sure that you understand the situation and the behaviour of the species.

Remember, injured animals are unpredictable. They are frightened and may do some real damage with their teeth or claws. Observe a strict no-touch policy with bats. *See Bats, this chapter.*

Protect your pets, protect wildlife

Wild animals can pose a risk to your beloved pets – by capturing them as prey, or by passing on diseases like rabies which might be present in the wild population. And, your pet can pose a risk to wildlife: household pets, especially cats, can inflict considerable damage on populations of birds and small mammals.

- Consider keeping your cat indoors. It keeps them from being both predator and prey; indoor cats are generally healthier and longer-lived than their outdoor cousins. It *is* possible to turn an outdoor cat into a content indoor cat.
- Hang your bird feeder at least 1.5 m (5 ft) above the ground.
- If you leave your dog outside, consider building a fenced run for it. It's easier on the dog than tying it up and safer, for both the dog and wildlife, than letting it run loose. Some dogs can create trouble by digging along the shoreline and harassing wildlife.
- Protect your water quality from the impact of your pets. Dispose of droppings in the garbage or flush them down the toilet. Remove pet waste from sidewalks or gutters where it will contaminate runoff, and enter nearby surface water.

⑫ Surviving the Seasons

Fall, Winter, Spring and Summer

***We** moved to the lake in mid-winter when the ground was covered with deep snow. As spring approached, and snow gradually melted, each day brought with it new bird calls. Then one day, the temperature shot up, and the thaw really started. We raced outside to enjoy the warm sun on our faces, only to be faced with a torrent of snow-melt pouring down the driveway, and heading straight for our door. We had to move into gear quickly to prevent a flood of water in the basement.*

By planning ahead to the next season, you can minimize the chance that you'll find yourself braving the mid-winter cold to deal with frozen water pipes, or rushing to divert floodwaters from your house in the spring. You will also have more time to enjoy the beautiful seasonal changes that take place along your shore!

Use the guide on the following pages to help you identify key tasks for each season.

Our seasonal guide commences in the fall, because during this season you'll need to think about both winter and spring to plan ahead. Even if you live in an area that receives little snow, consider reviewing the suggestions here; you might still be on the receiving end of upstream melt in the spring.

We also include a special guide for seasonal residents to help you close up a dwelling in the fall, so that when you return in spring, you'll hopefully find everything as you left it.

Your Seasonal Guide

FALL

Planning for runoff

Check your runoff control systems in the fall in anticipation of spring runoff. Check how drainage systems are working by walking your property during a rainstorm. *See Chapter 4.*

- Install any needed runoff control devices.
- Clear drainage ditches, swales and culvert ends of sediment, rocks and other debris which could block the flow of water.
- Clear eavestroughs and downspouts of debris.
- Clean out silt deposits along driveway runoff logs.
- Check that any water surge deflectors are in place.

Docks

Bring in your dock to protect it from being squeezed by ice. Designate a place above the high water mark where you can store your dock without damaging your shoreline buffer.

Planning for snow removal

Designate areas for piling snow which will minimize interference with spring runoff, to avoid any possible flooding problems in the spring.

Stake and mark any trees, shrubs, large rocks, runoff logs or other objects that could be damaged by snow removal equipment, or could damage your plough or snow blower.

Wildlife

To keep insects and small mammals out of your house over the winter, follow the tips on prevention and sealing in *Chapters 4 and 11.*

Fall leaves

Compost them or use a mulching mower; don't dump over banks or bluff edges into ravines or the water.

Plumbing

Make sure that water pipes, pumps and outside faucets are either well insulated or drained so they can withstand freezing. Protect unheated crawl spaces; insulate footings, if necessary, with styrofoam.

WINTER

Septic systems

Prevent compaction of snow on your drain field (e.g., by snowmobiles). Undisturbed snow cover provides good insulation; compacted snow melts slowly and can saturate your field. *See Chapter 5.*

Winter traction

For suggestions to keep your driveways and sidewalks safe see Chapter 10.

Garbage on ice

To help prevent garbage, and other debris left behind by visitors, from freezing into ice on rivers and lakes, join forces with a few neighbours to create a "Citizen's Patrol" to monitor ice and speak to visitors about garbage. Plan a shoreline clean-up early in the spring to help protect nesting shorebirds.

Winter recreation

Take care when accessing a frozen lake for skating, cross-country skiing, snowmobiling or tobogganing. Use your summer access trail, rather than direct paths over snow. Even through the covering of ice and snow, vegetation and bank structure can be damaged by winter traffic.

Wells and pumps

If you have a sump pump to deal with water in the basement, keep valuables off the floor, on shelves, or on wooden blocks, especially if you leave your house unattended.

High water

Prepare in the fall to manage spring runoff. *(See "Fall".)* Even in low snow areas, meltwater from upstream may add to runoff through your property.

High water and septic systems

Conserve water to reduce the volume going into your septic drain fields. High spring water tables and saturated ground may reduce the effectiveness of your system. *See Chapter 10 for tips on water conservation, Chapter 5 for septic tips.* **CAUTION.** If you suspect that the water table is higher than your septic drain field, contact your Environmental Health Officer. You could be contaminating surface water. *See Chapter 5.* Pump your tank in mid-summer. If you pump when the water table is high, the empty tank could float up.

Flood preparedness

If your home or property is at risk from flooding, contact your local emergency services for assistance. *See Appendix 1.*

Spring mud

Avoid using a muddy driveway; rake out ruts before they dry and harden.

Use planks or boards to create temporary boardwalks. This saves compacting the soil, and helps keep mud out of your house and car!

Docks

Hold off putting docks into the water until ground conditions have hardened, to prevent damage to the shoreline.

Spring cleanup

Remember to leave nature's debris when you do your spring clean-up! *See Pg 66.*

SPRING

Drought

If your well is at risk of failure during dry spells, minimize water use and supplement with other sources such as rainwater collection. *See Chapter 10 for water conservation tips. For maintaining a lawn during drought, see Chapter 7.*

Gardening

For tips on mulching and other gardening suggestions, see Chapter 10.

Summer recreation

See Chapter 14 for safety tips for children on shorelines, and tips for avoiding hazards associated with recreation, including boating, swimming, and fishing.

Low water

If you draw from a water body, check to make sure that the intake pipe extends well past the low water mark or below the lowest stream flow.

Move a floating dock out as water levels drop, to avoid being suddenly stuck high and dry!

Algal blooms

Nutrients from fertilizer runoff or septic leachate can make still waters more susceptible to algal growth. In hot, calm weather, blue-green algae can "bloom" in huge numbers on the surface and become visible. These blooms may be toxic to animals or people who drink the water.

- Keep pets and domestic animals away from the water during a bloom. Every year some cattle die from drinking water contaminated with blue-green algae.
- Avoid water contaminated with blue-green algae: do not drink it (boiling won't remove toxins), shower or do laundry with it, or wade or swim in it. Do not eat fish caught in contaminated water bodies.

SUMMER

Tips for Seasonal Residents

tip Use RV anti-freeze made with propylene glycol that is safe for water systems. Use the smallest amount needed to displace the water in traps, to reduce the phosphates going down the drain.

" *One winter the kids flooded the flattest part of our lawn for a skating rink. When it melted in spring, the area turned into a swamp. It turned out the rink had been over the septic distribution field.* "

Shoreline resident

tip Spring plumbing wake-up – Carefully reverse the draindown process, making sure the foot valve and check valves are working properly before you put them in the water, all drain plugs are in place, anti-freeze is flushed, and air bled out of the hot water tank.

Resources

Cottage Water Systems. 1993 and 1999. Burns, Max. Cottage Life Books. Toronto, Ontario.

The Cottage Book: A Collection of Practical Advice. 1991. Edwards, Frank B., Editor. Hedgehog Productions Inc., Newburgh, Ontario.

See Appendix 1 for complete Resources.

Shutting down plumbing for winter

To remove all water from appliance traps and pipes, you'll need to:

- Pull any lake intake pipe and foot valve so it won't be damaged by freezing. Remove and clean intake filter.
- Disconnect the pump; remove drain plugs, blow into primer hole to force out water, and grease plugs for storage. If you have any doubts check with a plumber, a plumbing supply store, or the pump manufacturer.
- Shut off the main water supply to your house or cottage. If the main shut-off is above the frost line, remove water from the line to below the frost level.
- Drain your pressure tank, if you have one.
- Drain the hot water tank. (Disconnect the power at the breaker before you drain it, to avoid burning out the element. If your tank is propane- or gas-fired, and you have any doubts about shut-down methods, obtain professional advice.)
- Drain water softener, filter, purifier, or anything else that holds water. Don't forget the icemaker in the fridge!
- Drain pumps built into your washing machine and dishwasher. Disconnect the washing machine hoses so they can drain. If they are too hard to drain, fill intake hose with just enough RV antifreeze to displace water, and switch on machine just long enough for pump to suck in antifreeze. Leave the taps open over the winter.
- Flush toilets to empty tanks; use a toilet plunger and then scoop out any water that remains in bowl and tank; use an old towel to blot up the last remaining water. Fill bowl to normal level with RV antifreeze.
- Drain all the water out of the cottage. Open every tap and drain plug, and remove "bleeder caps", to get all the water out. Use an air compressor to blow the last of the water out of the lines, or let gravity do the job. Remove plugs from bottom of traps beneath sinks and tubs. Once drained, replace plugs and refill traps with RV antifreeze.

- Examine the lines to ensure that there are no places where water could become trapped. If you find any potential trouble spots and you're not using an air compressor, pour a cup of RV antifreeze into the line.
- Pour RV antifreeze into shower drains.
- Avoid pumping your septic tank just before closing up the cottage. The bacteria and volume of water in the tank should be adequate to prevent the contents from freezing. If you have an effluent pump, check with the supplier or installer about any special winterizing treatment.
- Keep a record of what you've done (opening valves, taps, drain plugs, etc.) to ease your job in the spring.

For winterizing of other types of water systems, consult Resources section.

Storage

- TAKE ALL YOUR FOOD HOME – don't invite animals like mice in for the winter!
- Empty and clean the fridge and freezer; leave them with the doors propped slightly open and an open package of baking soda inside.
- Remove blankets and seal in plastic storage bins with pieces or strips of cedar – it smells great and is much less toxic than moth balls.
- Make sure your chimney flue is fitted with a proper screened cap to prevent animals from getting in.
- Remove paints and other chemicals that will be damaged by freezing.
- Empty your bathroom of products like shampoos that may freeze, making a mess.

Power

- To avoid problems of mildew over the winter, cool your place down and use a dehumidifier to remove moisture BEFORE you close for the winter.
- Turn off the main breaker unless you plan to leave power on to operate exterior motion lights, sump pumps, etc. In this case, turn everything else off at the breaker box; make sure you turn off the furnace, baseboard heaters, hot water tank and pump and shut off propane lines.

⑬ Planning for Visitors

When the Doorbell Rings

"The only time our well runs dry is when we have visitors," a neighbour once told me. "They just take our water for granted; long morning showers and frequent loads of laundry... they don't realize what it means to have to take care of your own water supply."

A shoreline is a magnet; it has drawn you – and it draws others. When you live close to water, visitors will at least occasionally be part of your lifestyle. Having guests might also be part of your daily routine if you've decided to run a Bed & Breakfast, or have an extra cabin or two that you rent out (to help pay for those waterfront property taxes!)

When visitors come, you will undoubtedly want their presence to be a positive one, with minimal impact on your property, water quality and wildlife. By steering them into activities that are compatible with your property's natural assets, you'll be able to help them enjoy what you have to offer, without having to alter what nature put there in the first place.

Protect Your Investment

 If you rent out to tenants on a long-term basis, consider providing them with information about some of the other topics covered in this book – such as appropriate cleaning products and vehicle maintenance.

⚠ **CAUTION**

If you make boats available to your guests, be sure to have enough life-jackets and other safety equipment available to meet safe boating standards.

 Consider following the environmental lead of major hotels: give your guests the choice of sending their wet towels to the laundry, or letting them dry and reusing them.

Provide a Green Guest Guide for visitors (available at www.livingbywater.ca).

Communicating to guests

Communicate to your guests what you need them to do to help protect your property. Sometimes you may have to repeat it in a couple of different ways – for example, a note about the need for water conservation in a friendly bathroom notice, as well as a flyer in the bedroom. Or, a small sign marking your shoreline buffer and asking people to stay on the path.

You may want to provide your guests with tips on:

- protecting your septic system *(Chapter 5)*
- conserving water *(Chapter 10)*
- handling garbage *(Chapter 11)*
- minimizing impact on wildlife *(Chapter 14)*
- green boating *(Chapter 14)*
- suggestions for children *(Chapter 14)*

We have developed a Green Guest Guide which is available for downloading from our website. You can customize this with information specific to your property. You can also download our friendly "biffy" notice for posting in the bathroom if you have a septic system.

Managing the extra impact of guests

⚠ **CAUTION: If you operate several guest units or Bed & Breakfast rooms, the impact of your guests on your property may be greater than if those rooms were occupied by members of your family:**

- Guests – especially children – spend lots of time outdoors on your shoreline where they may trample delicate vegetation.
- There is often more laundry associated with guests (especially if you operate a Bed & Breakfast).
- People on vacation may like to treat themselves with long showers and baths, and be less conserving of resources generally.
- You may find you clean bathrooms and bedrooms more thoroughly and more frequently when you have visitors using them.

Because of these factors, you'll want to manage the extra impact of guests upon your property:

- Provide shoreline access in a focussed area, rather than across your whole shoreline. Keep the remainder natural. Consider using floating, towable docks or swimming platforms. *See Chapter 9.*
- Make sure that your water and sewage treatment systems can handle the frequent showers, laundry and dishwasher use!
- If you are on a septic system:

  ⚠ **CAUTION: If you bring a room into use as a guest room, add extra bedrooms, or build a guest cottage, you may need to expand your septic system.** *See Chapter 5.*

  - If you have many extra loads of laundry (towels, sheets, etc.) consider sending it out to a laundry service.
  - If you have an operation which provides food service, use phosphate-free detergents in your dishwasher, especially if you are on a septic system.

- Keep bathrooms and other areas clean by using the basic cleaners in Chapter 10; minimize use of chemicals and be restrained in the use of disinfectant (for example, by spraying onto rags).

Promote Positive Experiences

Focus on what you have

By focussing on your property's unique qualities, you can help meet your guests' needs for relaxation, excitement, learning and renewal – without having to transform your property into something else.

- Share your knowledge and enthusiasm about the area with your guests.
- Help guests learn about the wonders of nature around you, to enhance their enjoyment. Consider offering them the use of identification guides, maybe even a set of binoculars, to help them discover the various forms of life to be found while exploring your shoreline.
- Help facilitate special experiences for your guests:
  - Offer dawn walks, late night campfires and stargazing.
  - Tell them about nearby walking trails; if you have a large property, provide pathways through upland areas. You can reduce the impact on your shoreline by providing visitors with enjoyable activities away from the water.
- Consider creating a central area closer to the water's edge for relaxation and events – benches with views, or even a small gazebo, strategically placed.
- Provide information about current fishing regulations, local boating restrictions and any other regulations guests need to be aware of. *See the tips for boating and recreation in Chapter 14.*

Protection first, density second

If you are considering developing a site into a small tourist operation:

- Be clear about your objectives and what values and features of your property you wish to protect or enhance. Provide this information to any professional you hire to assist you.
- Consider your customers and the uniqueness of your property when you plan. Guests will be much more satisfied and eager to return if you are able to create positive experiences for them.

⚠️ **CAUTION: *Resist any temptation to maximize the density of buildings, campsites or overnight guest rooms on your property.***

Remember, waterfront property is different. Fragile shorelines are easily harmed by high densities of people, often resulting in "hardened" shorelines – and thus creating potential problems in the future.

- Instead, consider a smaller number of higher value units, rather than maximum density. People are willing to pay for value – and that value is perceived to be a lower density, uncrowded tourist experience!
- Concentrate your development in one general area (cluster development), and keep the majority of your shoreline untouched.
- Keep your shoreline for all your guests to enjoy by placing all units back from the water.
- Develop your site in proportion to its size, maintaining areas of native vegetation. *See Chapters 4 and 7.*
- Create views through pruning of trees. Setting your home or cottages back in the trees offers lots of privacy, which may be exactly what your guests are looking for!
- Plan roads to keep vehicles away from sensitive areas, and keep them well back from the water's edge. Guests want to be able to look at the water, not vehicles!
- Keep any campsites well back from the water's edge.

Many of the tourist facilities developed in Alberta over the last fifty years were built close to the water's edge. To accommodate the pressure from people, shorelines were paved, grassed and hardened. Today, many tourists are interested in what experiences they can have – as well as enjoying a beautiful view. Focus on helping them enjoy themselves, and you'll be able to protect your property and avoid sacrificing your shoreline.

> ❝ *We took guests on a nature walk each week to introduce our 'Resort with a Difference' and to explain the reasons for our natural landscaping approach. People gave us feedback that learning the "why" helped them support what we were doing.* ❞
>
> Sarah and Clive

tip **Make sure your planned business conforms with land use zoning regulations, check whether you need a business licence, and update your home insurance coverage if you have paying guests in your home.**

> ❝ *By adding extras, such as the use of boats and canoes, childrens' campfire programs, guided nature walks and a variety of recreational equipment, we were able to increase the rental rates on cottages and maintain a low density atmosphere.* ❞
>
> Sarah and Clive

Resources

Cottages, Cabins and Chalets – An Owner's Guide for Guests. 1997. Chabanais, Paula, et al. Doubleday Canada Ltd., Toronto, Ontario.

See Appendix 1 for complete Resources.

Enjoying Your Waterfront

Boating, Fishing, Swimming...

I am an ardent canoeist, who loves the peaceful glide of the paddle in the water; I have a son who loves speed. The faster and more thrilling, the better! However, my son also loves fishing, and all the wild-life which inhabits shorelines. He would never knowingly destroy them or their habitat through his enjoyment of fast boats. So this chapter is for all those who enjoy having fun with water – in both fast and slow boats!

Boating is, for many of us, an integral part of our life by the water. But unless we're careful, the way we use and maintain our boats can have a big effect on the little piece of water we call home.

Fuel spills and poorly maintained or older engines can cost us a bundle as well as foul water and damage fish and wildlife habitat. That makes the other things we like to do by the water, like fishing and swimming, a lot less pleasant, or even impossible. And if we draw water for drinking, it can have serious health risks.

In this chapter we give tips for enjoying the water while at the same time protecting it, and shorelines. By following the Green Boater checklist and some of the chapter's other ideas, you can help minimize any negative effects boating might have on your shoreline. You'll be protecting your fishing grounds, and you'll save money on fuel.

We also include safety and etiquette tips, and some ideas for helping direct children's energy to keep them safe and happy, without damaging shoreline buffers or wildlife.

Boating

Green Boater Checklist

☐ Opt for the latest four-stroke or modern two-stroke-injection motor.

☐ Keep up with regular engine maintenance.

☐ Inspect fuel line, clamps, and filters monthly.

☐ Drive at a "no-wake" speed near shore.

☐ Fuel up away from water if your tanks are detachable.

☐ Choose non-toxic cleaners.

☐ Clean your boat well (on shore) when leaving the water.

☐ Use the least toxic hull paint possible.

☐ Reduce grey water release – if you have a cabin on your boat, add a holding tank.

☐ Never discharge black water.

☐ Use bilge pillows or absorbent pads to soak up oil, fuel, or antifreeze, or install a bilge filter.

☐ Take your garbage home.

☐ Remove any plants or animals that may be clinging to the hull, trailer or motor, or that are hiding in the bilge.

For more information see Resources at the end of the chapter.

> **tip** *The single most important thing that you can do to save on fuel costs and minimize water pollution is to upgrade your two-stroke engine. Most of these inefficient engines leave up to 25% of their oil and gas unburned, and leak it into the water instead.*

> Did you know ... *An older 70 hp two-stroke engine, operated for two hours, produces more airborne pollutants than driving 8,000 km in a car!*

Motors

- Consider upgrading your motor to a direct fuel injection two-stroke engine or a modern four-stroke that meets or betters the USA EPA emission standards for the year 2006. Four-stroke motors are often the best choice; they are well-sealed, quieter, produce very little smoke, and burn fuel most efficiently. You might even pay for the cost of the four-stroke engine in a few years with your savings on fuel, maintenance and repairs!

- Carry out regular engine maintenance to prevent leaking seals, gaskets or hoses. Collect all waste oils and antifreeze for recycling or disposal at most marinas or service stations.

- Try to go emission free! Consider having an electric motor on board with a battery and an outboard propeller, if you use your boat primarily for low-speed activities in calm water, such as trolling. Keep a tray under your battery to catch acid spills.

Operating your boat

- Within 150 m (500 ft) of shore, watch your wake at varying speeds and adjust your speed up or down accordingly. This will prevent waves which can erode banks and swamp nests.

- Within 30 m (100 ft) of shore on inland waters, conform to Canada Boating Restrictions, which limits all power-driven vessels to 10 km/h (5.4 knots or 6.2 mph). Some exceptions:
  - Vessels are allowed to travel perpendicularly from the shoreline to tow a skier, wakeboard, etc. out from shore, within designated areas (marked by buoys).
  - The regulation does not apply to rivers that are less than 100 m (350 ft) wide or in buoyed channels, but we recommend that you watch your wake in all situations!

- Turn off your propeller in shallow waters to avoid stirring up the bottom; get out your paddle, or stay clear of these areas entirely.

> **tip** *To change speed limits and motor types on a water body, petition your municipality to apply to the Canadian Coast Guard for a change in designation under the Navigable Waters Act. The Coast Guard regulates all navigable lakes and rivers.*

> **tip** *Familiarize yourself with Canada's Safe Boating Regulations and make sure your visitors are aware of them too. See Appendix 1.*

Did you know . . .

Oil or fuel spills on the water harm wildlife by: preventing the water from absorbing oxygen – vital to many water organisms; poisoning microscopic organisms living in surface water; damaging the water-protective feathers and coats of animals; and, poisoning them as they groom or preen.

> ❝ *We've found the difference between white – and really white! Pressure-washing our boat was like spraying white paint over the surface. To think we spent all those years scrubbing!* ❞
>
> Boat owner

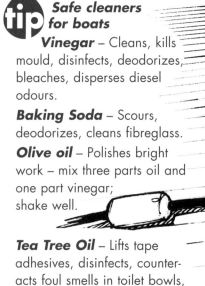

tip

Safe cleaners for boats

Vinegar – Cleans, kills mould, disinfects, deodorizes, bleaches, disperses diesel odours.

Baking Soda – Scours, deodorizes, cleans fibreglass.

Olive oil – Polishes bright work – mix three parts oil and one part vinegar; shake well.

Tea Tree Oil – Lifts tape adhesives, disinfects, counteracts foul smells in toilet bowls, shower sumps and bilges.

Wrap a fuel absorbent cloth around the nozzle when refueling, to prevent spills.

- Be aware of the noise your engine produces and be considerate of others.
- Give all wildlife space; stay clear of nesting or resting birds and other wildlife on or near shore.

Fuel with care

The most common polluting event on the water is a spill of diesel fuel or gasoline while refuelling.

- Whenever possible fill portable, and engine mounted, fuel tanks on shore. This will prevent direct spills into the water.
- Install an anti-surge valve in the fuel vent line to prevent fuel from leaking overboard.
- Know the capacity of your tank; have an accurate fuel gauge.
- Fill slowly and listen to the change in tone as the tank fills. Use your hand to check for air escaping the vent. A distinct change in the air flow will signal you to stop filling.
- Avoid "topping-off" or overfilling. Excess fuel can escape through the vent line.
- Be prepared for spills, as they will almost always end up in the water.
  - Wrap a fuel absorbent pad or a cloth around the nozzle before moving it to catch any spills from the filler pipe.
  - Wedge an absorbent pad into the scupper on the same side as the filler pipe to ensure that if any fuel escapes you will have time to clean it up before it can run into the water.
  - Place another pad at the fuel tank vent.

Spills

Even a small spill of fuel or oil in the water can spread quickly over a large area. In one case, a spill which covered 1,100 sq m (12,000 sq ft) was estimated to have been caused by 300 ml (a little over 1 cup). Fuel docks and marinas must have spill control equipment (absorbent cloths and booms) on hand.

- Report spills or oil sheens of any size to the Canadian Coast Guard at 1-800-889-8852. The call will be relayed to an Environmental Response duty officer in your area. You may be asked when, where and how the spill happened, the nature of the spill, an estimate of volume, area covered and the name of the person or boat that caused the spill.

Cleaning your boat

- Frequently wash your boat with fresh water and a soft brush, to reduce the build-up of dirt while minimizing the amount of toxic paint released into the water. Wash your boat on a surface where the runoff will not flow into surface water or storm sewers; a lawn works well, and will also benefit from the water.
- A power-washer is the ideal tool for cleaning non-slip surfaces. They are available for use at most marinas, or consider buying a portable one for regular use.
- Try out alternative cleaners. *See sidebar and Chapter 10 for more information.*
- Use detergents only when absolutely necessary and choose ones that are phosphate-free and non-petroleum based. Clean your boat away from the water if possible.
- Apply a good coat of boat wax to keep surface dirt from becoming ground in.

Maintaining the hull

If you trailer your boat to the ocean you will want to keep the hull free from growth in order to reduce drag and to maintain adequate freeboard. Marine antifoulants are by definition very toxic to aquatic life. Older-style antifouling paints contain heavy metals which slowly leach out of the paint to discourage growth. New non-fouling paints discourage growth by presenting a smooth surface that makes it difficult for organisms to attach to.

- Pressure wash your hull at marinas which have wastewater collection systems; these are hard to find, but as customer demand increases, so will services.

- Replace antifoulants with silicon and teflon-based paints followed by a coat of slick bottom wax. Teflon and silicon paints are best used when the boat has a smooth hull and is not permanently in the water, e.g., a trailered boat.

- If you use an antifoulant, use a copper-in-epoxy product. These are less toxic than the other heavy metal-based paints.

- Hard bottom paints require sanding and surface preparation prior to re-painting. Use a drop cloth to collect the residue and, for small amounts, dispose of it with regular waste. If you have over 5 kg (11 lbs) of toxic residue, contact a hazardous waste disposal firm.

- Avoid spilling paint or varnish into water and paint only above the high water mark, again using a drop cloth.

- Look for Paint Care programs in your area. They will take left-over marine enamel paint. Take marine antifouling paint to a household hazardous waste depot in your area or, even better, store it carefully and save for future use.

Managing wastewater

If you have a larger boat with a cabin, try to minimize contamination of water by grey water (wastewater produced when showering and doing dishes on your boat).

- Whenever possible use facilities on shore to reduce the amount of detergent and soap entering the water. Conservative use of water is the first step in reducing grey water.

- Scrape food wastes into the garbage or compost bin, and soak dishes as soon as possible. If plates are greasy, wipe with paper towels before applying pure soap.

- Install holding tanks. If your water use is low, these can be transportable.

- Clean your shower screen and pump. This will extend the life of the pump, and improve the quality of any grey water. If your shower drains directly into the bilge, consider installing a shower sump and holding tank.

Prevent contamination of water from untreated sewage, or "black water". If released into waterways, this is a health hazard for both people and wildlife. Shellfish, in particular, become contaminated with bacteria from human waste from the water.

- Fit your toilet with a holding tank. Modern tanks with hard poly-pipe plumbing and odour-resistant hoses combined with good aeration have all but eliminated the notorious smell of holding tanks.

- If your boat is equipped with dual system "Y-valves", lock the valves in a position that directs sewage to the holding tank. Better yet, remove the Y-valve as these are often the source of obnoxious holding tank odours.

- If you absolutely must use a holding tank treatment, use only non-toxic, biodegradable products such as those that use bacteriological action to break down waste. Avoid products with strong fragrances and chemicals like formaldehyde and chlorobenzene. They can interfere with the bacterial breakdown process and are toxic to aquatic life.

- Fasten portable toilets securely to the boat and have a permanent fixture enabling them to be emptied at a pump-out station.

 CARE OF THE HEAD 250 ml (1 c) of vinegar mixed with 65 ml (1/4 c) of baking soda will clean and deodorize your toilet just as well as a commercial cleaner.

⚠️ **CAUTION**
When boating, watch for "NO DISCHARGE ZONES". All pleasure boats with on-board toilets entering these areas must have holding tanks. Discharge of raw or chemically treated sewage is prohibited. *See Appendix 1.*

❝ *The idea of having the holding tank located under our berth wasn't very appealing, but the thought of dumping sewage into the water was even less so. The tank has been in place for a year now and we haven't had an odour problem. We pump it frequently and occasionally add an environmental deodoriser.* ❞

Shoreline resident

 ⚠️ **CAUTION**
You can be prosecuted for dumping waste overboard in Canadian waters under the Canada Shipping Act, and under Alberta's Environmental Protection Act.

Careful boat cleaning can prevent the spread of Eurasian water milfoil and zebra mussels.

⚠️ **CAUTION**
Avoid bilge cleaners – even biodegradable ones. And NEVER add detergents to a fuel spill. They disperse diesel fuel into the water, making it impossible to clean up, and easier for aquatic organisms to ingest.

💧 *Ask your local marina to offer environmental services such as bilge pump-outs.*

⚠️ **CAUTION**
Prevent the spread of zebra mussels from affected areas (e.g., lakes in eastern Canada):
•Pressure wash your boat, tackle, downrigger cables, and trailer with hot water. Flush hot water (41°C /106°F) through the motor's cooling system and other boat parts that get wet.
•Let dry for five days before taking your boat to another water body.

Bilges

Bilges can contain engine oil, fuel, antifreeze, and transmission fluid – all toxic to plants, wildlife ... and people!

- Fit a tray underneath the engine, if possible, to contain any spills.
- Use disposable bilge cloths for cleaning out oily residues. These can be squeezed out into a container and re-used. Be sure to wear gloves as this residue is extremely toxic. Dispose of the liquid in a used oil collection facility.
- Turn off automatic bilge pumps. Use them only when required and when the bilge water is uncontaminated.
- Consider installing an in-line filter on your overboard discharge hose.
- Find marinas which offer a bilge pump-out service. This is your very best option!
- Only use bio-bilge or enzyme cleaners as a last resort.

Solid waste

Keep garbage on board until appropriate land disposal (composting, recycling, etc.) is available. "Pack in, pack out" – the same as if you were camping in any delicate area.

- Waste management starts at the grocery store. Choose goods with little or no packaging to reduce the need for storing garbage in the first place.

- Unpack goods and store them in air-tight containers before you leave. This also will deter unwanted boarders like insects.
- Have a specific spot on board where you can store sorted garbage and washed recyclables.
- Be especially careful with plastic waste, which is very hard on aquatic life.
- Never throw anything overboard, even food scraps. These can alter the environment in enclosed bays and tend to float up on shore before decomposing.

Trailering your boat

If you are considering buying a boat, make sure you buy the size that is right for your lifestyle. A small boat may provide the same enjoyment on the water as a large one, but cost a lot less to buy and maintain. You can always rent a big boat for those special occasions.

If you do own a small boat, making the most of your trailer will free you from having to put in a dock or pay for moorage. Keeping your boat on the trailer and out of the water will also reduce the time and money you spend on maintenance.

- To help keep your trailer in good condition, only enter the water as far as necessary and try to minimize the length of time the trailer is submerged. This will also reduce the amount of pollution that enters the water from your trailer.
- When you haul the boat out, remove any plants or animals that may be clinging to the hull, trailer or motor, or that are hiding in the bilge. The spreading of alien invader plants and animals such as Eurasian milfoil or zebra mussels can quickly alter your water body for the worse.

Fishing

If you enjoy fishing – or eating fish! – protecting fish and their habitat will be especially important for you.

Catching fish

- Remember to obtain a fishing licence, Sport Fishing Regulations for Alberta, and check on the regulations for your area. Catch limits and seasons vary for each region.

- Keep only full-size fish and release the small ones for next year!

- Learn how to catch and release fish so they have the best chance of survival.

- Help your children learn good fishing techniques:
  - Teach your children humane ways of catching, handling and killing fish.
  - Make sure they are aware of daily limits and any other regulations which apply to the area in which they are fishing.
  - Consider using barbless hooks for children; it protects them should they snag a hook in themselves.
  - Help young fishers learn to cast properly to minimize accidental losses of fishing line into the environment where it will harm wildlife. *See Resources.*

- Generally, do not clean fish in lakes or streams, and bury fish guts upland at least 30 m (100 ft) from the shore instead of disposing of them in the water. This waste can add excess nutrients to the water. In winter, dispose of fish remains by freezing them and carrying them to the garbage.

Bait and gear

- Be extra careful to take all of your fishing line and lures back with you. Wildlife can ingest even small pieces of line, or easily become ensnared in it.

- Use lead-free fishing sinkers and jigs; these can be purchased at reputable retail stores that sell fishing tackle.

- Bait and containers may contain non-native, or invasive plant seed hitchhikers in with the worms. Dispose of containers in the garbage.

- Wash waders, fishing gear and containers after use to prevent the spread of invasive plants and animals.

 CAUTION

Avoid spreading animals or plants from one waterway to another:
- **Remove plants and animals from your boat, trailer and accessories.**
- **Drain your livewell and bilge before leaving the water.**
- **Empty your bait bucket on land, never in the water. Never dip your bait bucket into a water body if it has water in it from another. And, *never* dump live bait from one water body into another.**

 Did you know ...

A loon can die from ingesting even one lead sinker. In eastern North America up to one-half of all loon deaths are caused by eating lead sinkers and jigs.

tip *If you are considering a visit to B.C., check with the 24-hour Shellfish Information line or the DFO website if you plan to harvest shellfish. See Appendix 1.*

 CAUTION

Obtain medical attention immediately if a person who has eaten shellfish feels tingling or numbness of the lips or tongue. This is a symptom of paralytic shellfish poisoning, caused by red tide (a concentration of toxin-containing phytoplankton).

Teach children ways of protecting fish and fish habitat.

Shoreline Safety and Etiquette

tip *Consider the safety and environmental aspects of Personal Water Craft (PWC) if you are considering a purchase. Check for restrictions on their use in your area. Opt for a motor that meets or betters the EPA 2006 standards.*

> *Our three-year-old fell off the dock one April morning when "helping" his dad do some work. Fortunately he was wearing a PFD and just got a cold lesson.*
>
> Sarah and Clive

Did you know . . .

"Swimmer's itch" is a temporary rash some people get when swimming in affected lakes and ponds. It is caused by the immune system trying to destroy a tiny parasite that normally lives on waterfowl and snails.

tip *To help prevent swimmer's itch, apply waterproof suntan lotion and towel off vigorously or shower immediately after swimming. If you get a rash, apply calamine lotion, zinc ointment or lavender essential oil to soothe the itch.*

Water-based recreation is associated with many accidents each year; activities such as boating, swimming, diving and other water sports each have inherent risks. As a waterfront resident you, as well as your family and guests, will be exposed to these risks. Develop common-sense safety practices, and make sure that you know of any hazards specific to your area. As well, practise common-sense etiquette.

Boating safety
- Make sure boaters are aware of hazards in your area – rocks, submerged logs, shoals, dangerous currents, or potential for sudden storms.
- Keep boats properly equipped and fuelled, and motors well maintained.
- Use charts.

Hazards of exploring shorelines
- On rivers and lakes, be wary of risks associated with thin ice – when walking, skating, ice fishing, or driving with ATVs or snowmobiles.
- In coastal waters, make sure you and your visitors are familiar with tide charts, and know times of incoming and outgoing tides before venturing out.
- Use common sense when exploring shoreline bluffs and cliffs.

Swimming
- Make sure that young children wear a Personal Flotation Device (PFD) any time they are on a dock or playing down by the water's edge.
- Keep a reach pole or paddle and life jackets handy for rescues.
- Use inflatable toys carefully. Wind and currents can quickly blow children into deep water.
- Mark where the water is safe for swimming (perhaps with small buoys). Be very careful of swift currents and undertow, especially on rivers. Make sure that children walk out and swim parallel to the shore, never straight out into deep water.

- Watch out for swimmer's itch on some lakes. *See sidebar.*
- Make sure children wear sunscreen or protective clothing when they play outside and near water. Water reflects sunlight, so the potential for serious sunburn is great.

Harmful plants and animals
- Learn to identify plants like stinging nettle that can be found along shorelines, especially if you have children.

Contaminated water
- Avoid swimming in waters contaminated by fecal coliforms (usually from leaking septic systems or other sources of human sewage, although beaver or muskrat can also be a factor).
- Also avoid swimming in waters affected by blue-green algal blooms. *See Chapter 12.*

Campfire safety
- Always use caution with any fire, even though you are near a water body. Sudden winds can pick up cinders and start a fire in dry grass or undergrowth amazingly quickly.
- Keep your fire small, and have quick access to water for dousing should it suddenly burn out of control. Avoid burning beach driftwood which may be part of your shoreline protection, and don't burn treated or painted wood.

Children and shorelines
Children can unknowingly damage vegetation and harass wildlife in their quest to explore the natural world.
- Remind them frequently of the 3 Ls: Look, Learn, and Leave them alone. Encourage children to observe from a distance, perhaps by providing them with binoculars.
- Remind children to be gentle with the shoreline; damming streams, disturbing bottom mud or gravel, collapsing banks, destroying vegetation or harassing fish and other wildlife harm the very thing they wish to explore.

- Identify areas for play which are less likely to be damaged, especially in spring, when plants are easily trampled and soil compacted. Suggest areas for projects like forts, and what materials children can use. Make sure they leave some deadfall for wildlife.
- Direct some of their energy into projects like building a bat house or a bird house. *See Chapter 11 and Appendix 1 for some suggestions.*

Shoreline etiquette

Look

- Give wildlife some space. Animals are easily disturbed by noise and visitors, which may result in nest abandonment. Keeping your distance also gives you a better chance to observe something interesting.
- Leave fallen trees and logs, even shells, rocks and pieces of vegetation where they lie. Many shoreline creatures use them for protection.

Learn

- Obtain books, identification guides, videos and other materials to help you learn about the wildlife you see.
- Identify any sensitive areas (such as new plant growth or wildlife nesting sites) and observe from a safe distance.

Identify and record your discoveries, instead of removing them from their natural environment.

Leave them alone

- Leave the wildlife that you find on shorelines alone. For example:
  - Minnows will quickly die in a bucket as the water warms up.
  - The skin of amphibians is very delicate and can be easily harmed by human contact.

⚠ **CAUTION: *Never move animals from one shore to another.***

- "Take only pictures and leave only footprints." Take your garbage – and consider taking other garbage that you find.

Step carefully

- Try to step on bare spaces free of plants and animals.
- If you turn over a rock or log, especially below the high water line, put it back the way you found it so the creatures living on its underside aren't exposed to the sun.
- Fill in any holes that you dig.
- Keep motor vehicles and even bicycles off beaches.

tip *When entering or leaving ice-covered lakes or rivers on an ATV or snowmobile:*
- *Avoid breaking down bluffs, banks and shoreline vegetation.*
- *Stay away from these sensitive areas during the spring thaw when the ground is wet and muddy, and susceptible to rutting and erosion.*

Resources

Guide to Green Boating. 2000. Georgia Strait Alliance. www.georgiastrait.org/ CleanBoating/guidep1.htm

The Enviro-Boater Guide: A Guide to Environment-friendly Boating. 1995. Canadian Power and Sail Squadrons. www.cps-ecp.ca

Children's Angler Education Program www.fishsmart.org (604) 666-6512

Kids Cottage Book. 1993. Drake, Jane and Anne Love. Kids Can Press Ltd., Toronto, Ontario.

See Appendix 1 for complete Resources.

15 Reservoirs and Dams

The Ups and Downs of Living With Them

A colleague lives on a lake controlled by a dam for irrigation. Because high water occurs only infrequently, it has been easy for some shoreline residents to forget how high the water can come. If they have lawns, they mow them a little closer to the water's edge each year. But if high water comes and coincides with a storm and big waves, there is little erosion protection left, and away goes their bank.

If you live by water, or are thinking about moving to a lake, river or creekside, check whether water levels are influenced by a dam. You may find that one of Alberta's dams is at work near you!

If your property is located on a reservoir or downstream of a dam, you are part of a controlled system – one which has probably been altered from its natural state. Water levels may fluctuate and fish and other wildlife habitat change, sometimes imperceptibly, but sometimes with great speed.

While dam safety regulations have been set in place, dams themselves are considered by law to be "inherently dangerous structures". Some dams have been built to protect downstream land from flooding, but in exchange, if you live downstream of one, you must be prepared for the possibility – no matter how remote – of the dam leaking or even breaking.

Check to find out if you live on a controlled waterway, and if you do, who looks after the dam and reservoir. You'll know where you can go to for help; then you'll be able to relax and enjoy living on your unique piece of shore.

Buying on a Controlled Waterway

Do your homework and research the area before you buy and make a big move. Check with neighbours and others in the area about how the dam operation affects their property – in particular, water levels, erosion, and wildlife habitat.

Water levels

The change in water level from summer to winter "pool" is different for each reservoir, and for each downstream waterway. The up and down movement of water in the reservoirs is affected by many factors:

- the seasons
- climatic cycles (drought, flooding)
- demand for electricity
- licensing obligations such as irrigation
- recreational uses
- habitat protection and wildlife management (fish spawning, nesting, etc.)

If year-round views of a beautiful shoreline are important to you, make sure you know what the winter water levels are going to be before you purchase land on a reservoir. On some lakes, for example, your fabulous view of the water in the summer could disappear as the water retreats in winter to a distant trickle as much as a kilometre away. Additionally, in a dry year when summer lake levels are low, sediment left behind may be disturbed by winds, resulting in "dust bowl storms".

Before purchasing, check the property's boundaries – especially with respect to water levels. Investigate the land title carefully and obtain copies of any easements. There will probably be a caveat registered on the title by the dam owner or operator. The caveat will indicate the area flooded when the reservoir is at full supply and at emergency flood levels. Any erosion below this contour line is considered a normal consequence of the operation of the dam and reservoir. There are usually development restrictions and setbacks associated with the flood area so check with your local municipality. Make sure you don't place buildings or other structures below the full supply line.

Erosion and debris

Erosion may be a concern when you buy property on or downstream of a reservoir:

- The repeated wetting and drying along the shoreline breaks up soil structure.
- Cycles of flooding and extreme dryness mean that vegetation has a difficult time surviving and cannot buffer the shoreline from the effects of the water flow.
- Strong water flows may sweep away any protective vegetation that does grow.

There may also be concerns about excessive debris interfering with boating or being deposited on your shoreline, as a result of the flooding of a valley. The amount of debris tends to decrease as a reservoir ages.

> *We have heard stories of people on reservoirs who lived through a number of low water years and forgot how high the water could rise. In one case, someone lost a shed.*
>
> Sarah and Clive

Things to Know about Controlled Waterways

- **Dam owners are responsible for the safe operation and maintenance of their dams and are financially liable for any damage to land and property resulting from failure of their dam.**

- **In late fall, the water level in a reservoir is lowered and shoreline is exposed. This allows room in the reservoir for storing water from spring rains and snow melt. The reservoir gradually fills up again to a level that is held throughout the summer.**
  Jan–Mar   Levels at lowest
  Apr–Jul   Levels rise to max
  Aug–Dec   Levels drop

Living on a Controlled Waterway

> *I only use my floating dock until mid-July. After that, the water levels usually drop too much for me to use it.*
>
> Shoreline resident

Resources

Reservoir Lands Guideline. Alberta Environment. www3.gov.ab.ca/env/water/ Reports/ReservoirLandsGuideline.pdf

See Appendix 1 for complete Resources.

Living with erosion

To help reduce the negative effects of erosion along your shoreline:

Maintain and enhance shoreline vegetation to help decrease the severity of erosion. While this can sometimes be a challenge on a controlled waterway, vegetation is one of the best ways to control erosion.

- Follow tips elsewhere in this book for minimizing damage from construction, recreation and other activities.
- Leave debris in place as much as feasible. It may actually help you in the battle against erosion.
  - Logs, stumps and branches can protect your shoreline from the scouring effect of fast-moving water.
  - Debris helps provide habitat for aquatic animals such as small fish and frogs.
  - Vegetation may find it easier to become established in the shelter of debris.

Wildlife habitat

The changes to wildlife habitat along the shores of lakes and rivers affected by dams can be immense, both upstream and downstream of the dam. In some reservoirs, as water levels drop, mud flats become exposed. The silt is stirred up, the water becomes cloudy, and fish are forced to move away from the shoreline area and into deeper water – a less suitable habitat.

To protect fish and other wildlife habitat:

- Protect streams flowing into the lake or river you are on.
- Work to maintain natural vegetation on your property as much as possible.
- Contact local groups who may be working on habitat enhancement projects.

Boating

- Be safety aware: seasonal water level fluctuations can make boating dangerous – previously navigable channels may disappear at low water times.
- Anchored and floating debris is a hazard at all times, and at all water levels. In particular watch for stumps during low water.
- If you beach your boat or tie it up at a dock, be aware that if the water level drops during the night, you could be "high and dry" in the morning, or conversely, if the water rises, your boat may have wandered. For information about daily water levels, contact the local dam office. *See Appendix 1.*
- Take care when boating immediately downstream or upstream of a dam. Water can be released without warning, altering water levels dramatically and creating strong underwater currents and turbulence. The currents created upstream can be strong enough to pull you under the water and trap you against the intake structures of the dam.
- Ensure that the boat ramp you wish to use is in operation before you go. Low water levels may leave some boat ramps exposed beyond use.

Docks

If you are on a water body with radical changes in water levels, you may wish to consider the economics of constructing a dock that may be usable for only part of the boating season. The most practical type of dock is a small section of floating dock (on a cable and anchor system) that you move regularly as water levels change. Long docks with a ramp to a floating platform are expensive to build and maintain; plus, Alberta Sustainable Resource Development and other agencies are unlikely to approve them.

16 Waterside Hobby Farms and Woodlots

Protecting Water Quality

While writing this book we attended a workshop for ranchers and farmers on caring for the "green zone". A farmer who had moved from a dry area to a riverside property described his experience. When he bought, he was pleased he'd found land with a year-round source of water – he'd worry less about his cattle. Then his neighbours came by. "You've bought a lemon", they said. "You won't be able to do anything without fisheries and environment officials breathing down your neck." When he went to meet some of these officials, they offered to send him to a "Cows and Fish" course. He now looks at rivers very differently, and spoke convincingly about how farmers can have efficient operations – and protect watercourses.

Do you have an orchard or a market garden – maybe to earn just enough income to maintain your farm status? Or perhaps you have a couple of horses, and don't even think of yourself as a hobby farmer! Or you occasionally harvest trees as a source of income.

Water is often a part of a hobby farm or a woodlot – whether it's a lake, a wetland or a small creek that runs through your property. It's in your long term financial interest to manage your property to protect water quality. This chapter focusses on providing a few tips around "best management practices" to help you do this. (Also read other chapters in the book if your house is close to water.)

You probably will have thought about how you can use different areas of your land to generate revenue, and may have considered potential uses such as pasture, cropland, timber, firewood, berries, or vegetables for the farmer's market. As well as providing benefits for you, your land is part of a larger picture – a complex web of life. Whether it's meadow or grassland, forested, cleared or some combination of these, the trees, shrubs, perennial plants and grasses on your land play other roles. They provide places for wildlife to seek refuge, build homes and find food. Vegetation bordering the water's edge protects land and water quality, and protects downstream users from problems.

Planning

Assessing your land

Evaluating your property's characteristics will help you plan how to use it, and identify whether there are additional things you can do to help protect it in the long run. Assess whether your property is suitable for the uses you plan to make of it.

- Is it large enough for both your present and future needs, with an adequate and suitable resource base (soils, timber)?
- Are there areas unsuitable for your intended use – e.g., sensitive wetlands?
- Will you be able to comply with legislated setback requirements?

Carrying out a planning exercise may help you increase productivity over the long term, prevent costly mistakes, protect water quality for you and your neighbours, prevent erosion problems, and enhance wildlife habitat.

Establishing buffer zones

If you've read Chapter 3, you'll know that establishing buffer zones around water helps to protect your property. Buffer zones help keep sediment and pollutants like manure and pesticides out of your water, reduce erosion, and protect habitat for wildlife.

- Establish a no-use, no-harvest buffer as close as possible to the minimum width that we recommend on Pg 13. We recognize that in cleared areas this may be difficult to achieve; whatever protection you can provide will be a start. Increase the width of the buffer if slopes are steep, soil is easily eroded, and the land is adjacent to sensitive water bodies.
- Keep access routes to fields well back from the shoreline.
- Plan drainage to protect the buffer and surface water; *see diagram.*

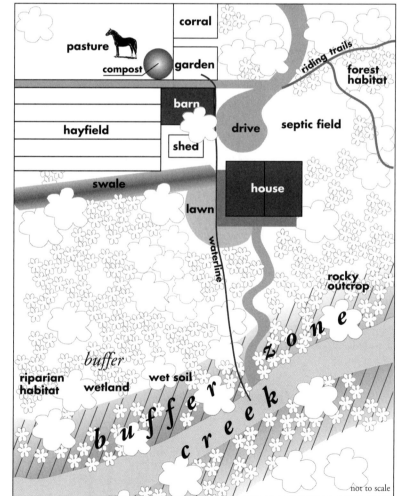

Planning a hobby farm or woodlot

Managing Your Animals

Watering

Clean, fresh water is as vital for animal health as it is for yours. The buffer, your most powerful protective tool, can be quickly damaged if livestock have uncontrolled access to the water's edge. Options include:

- Using appropriate fencing to limit animal access to surface water and shorelines.
- Building a sloped and gravelled water access with a cross-stream fence. This will protect the rest of the water's edge from damage. Or better, use an off-stream watering system. Many of these will operate without electricity, and some will work year-round.
- Building your watering facility on a concrete pad to prevent muddying the surrounding area; pipe overflow away. If necessary, use a berm to divert runoff from surface water.
- Drawing livestock away from sensitive areas by providing shade beyond the shoreline zone with trees, or a shelter.

Feeding

Balance livestock numbers with the amount of pasture you have. Overgrazing your pasture will reduce productivity and create bare spots, exposing soil to invasion by weeds and increasing the risk of soil loss through erosion.

- Locate paddocks, feedlots and feeding areas at least 50 m (165 ft) from waterways and wetlands, in well drained areas not subject to seasonal flooding.
- Place feed supplements such as salt or mineral blocks as far away as possible from streams to reduce loitering near banks.
- Divert runoff away from the feeding area, and divert contaminated runoff from the feeding area away from surface water.

Managing manure

Manure applied properly to pasture or cropland can save money on chemical fertilizers. If it is managed and stored well, you'll protect animal health, and prevent problems of water contamination, as well as complaints from neighbours.

Storing manure

- Ensure that you have enough land to store and spread your animals' manure.
- Locate your storage area at least 50 m (165 ft) from any watercourse, lake, well or domestic water sources.
- Store raw manure and compost under cover, on an impervious level pad, at least 1 m (3 ft) above the water table, or 1.5 m (5 ft) above the 100 year flood level, whichever is higher. The storage area needs to be big enough to hold the manure generated during the fall and winter. Avoid spreading it during these seasons when fields are saturated or frozen.

Keep manure out of water, and water out of manure

Divert clean water (e.g., from uphill runoff) to avoid contact with dirt and manure.

- Use low, grassed, mowable swales, ditches, or berms; they are easily installed, yet effective in keeping clean water out of manure areas. *See Chapter 4 for other ideas on dealing with runoff.*
- Seed long grasses along natural water flow paths or runoff courses in cropped fields. This will help slow down water, prevent soil erosion, and absorb pollutants.
- Maintain shrubs and grasses around corrals to help trap and absorb dirty runoff.
- Consider constructing small wetland "pockets" to intercept runoff ditches and swales prior to runoff entering main watercourses. They can even make your property more attractive.
- If possible, use land that floods in the spring for crops rather than for pasture, to avoid manure washing into surface water.
- When spreading manure, keep it 50 m (165 ft) back from wells, springs, water intakes, and streams. Avoid applying it to areas where there is standing water, on slopes where surface runoff is likely, on very windy days, and late in the day when cool air is settling (morning is better when warm air is rising).

> *" The vet told me that removing manure from my animals' area to a separate compost pile will reduce the number of worms they pick up from grazing. This reduces their need for medication, as well as the number of flies that bother them. It also helps protect our lake water. "*
>
> Shoreline resident

tip *Treat manure like an unmarked bag of fertilizer – when you store it, and when you apply it. Use soil and manure tests to determine nutrient quantities and application rates.*

Did you know ...
To comply with provincial regulations under the Environmental Protection Act, manure must be stored in a manner to prevent pollution.

tip *Follow the "Grazing rule of thumb" – "Take half, leave half". Remove livestock from pastures when grass is 8-10 cm (3-4 in) to encourage rapid regrowth. Regraze only when grass has grown to at least 16 cm (6 in) high.*

Caring for Cropland

tip *Keep animals and machinery off wet soil. Soil can easily become compacted in wet weather or when the water level is high, increasing the chance of erosion and decreasing the soil's ability to absorb water.*

> *" My cattle are suffering with far fewer flies since I let some native plants take over along the fence line between two fields. Between that and the buffer along the creek, I'm getting lots of bats and birds – even dragonflies. "*
>
> Shoreline resident

tip *If your property is close to an urban, semi-urban or recreational area, avoid potential complaints from your neighbours about water contamination, pesticide drift, odour, noise, dust and flies. Keep lines of communication open, and follow Best Management Practices.*

Did you know ...
A water licence is normally required to withdraw water for irrigation purposes from any surface water source in Alberta.

Keep soil healthy

Rotate crops and add organic matter to maintain soil structure. Your soil will be more fertile, with reduced runoff and erosion since water will be absorbed more easily. Soil erosion decreases crop yields and property values, and increases land management costs. It also pollutes water.

- Minimize fall tillage and avoid keeping land bare over the wet season. If you keep at least a third of your soil surface covered with crop stubble and plant residues (mulch), soil erosion will be reduced and your soil will hold more moisture.
- Plant a winter crop or green manure, and, wherever possible, plant a cover crop between rows.
- Till and plant along the contours of sloping fields to reduce downhill movement of soils and water.
- Ensure fertilizers do not run off fields into nearby watercourses.

Using pesticides

Keep soil healthy and rotate crops so that plants have the greatest chance of being healthy.

- Instead of using pesticides, enhance habitat for natural predators of pests by increasing the native vegetation on your property.

If you have considered the alternatives, but feel you need to use pesticides, follow best management practices for their application. Take an integrated pest management approach. *See Appendix 1.*

- Store your pesticides in a concrete building, on a high site with all natural runoff draining away from the site. The building should have a sill to contain spills and should not have floor drains. Prepare a spill management plan and ensure you have equipment and supplies on hand for cleaning up.
- To protect shoreline vegetation and surface water, establish a pesticide-free buffer zone **in addition to** your shoreline buffer zone of at least 15 m (50 ft) beside all watercourses, water bodies, wells and water sources, including ditches. This provides for additional space back from the buffer zone to allow for spray drift.

Irrigation

Many streams naturally have low summer flows, so using their water for irrigation can have a major impact on aquatic habitat.

- To make efficient use of water, irrigate based on crop need, as determined by careful monitoring of soil moisture, weather, and crop growth.
- If you have the choice, take water from a larger rather than smaller stream, and a warmer rather than cooler one.
- Use mandatory fish screens if pumping from surface water so that fish aren't destroyed and they don't block the system.
- Give pumps good support to prevent damage to stream banks.
- If you are using your irrigation system to apply fertilizers or pesticides, use a backflow device to prevent back-siphoning.

Drainage

- Reduce long-term maintenance costs and minimize impacts on the environment with well designed drainage systems.
- Operate your irrigation system to avoid surface runoff and erosion.
- Use good management practices to minimize chemicals in drainage water.
- Protect wetland areas and use swales and constructed ponds to minimize the need for new ditches.
- Provide a vegetation buffer along at least one side of a ditch (south or west bank) to shade the ditch. Carry out maintenance from the other side.
- Never burn vegetation alongside lakes, wetlands or streams. Burning may kill desirable plants and encourage the growth of invasive plants. Nutrient-containing ash may wash into surface water.

Fuel and tanks

- Keep fuel tanks at least 50 m (165 ft) from drains, wells, ditches and watercourses.
- Protect fuel tanks from damage by vehicles and equipment; padlock valves to prevent vandalism.
- Equip tanks with devices to prevent spillage from overfilling; provide a dike around them to contain spills.

Managing a Waterside Woodlot

To maximize revenue from your resource over the long term, you will want to keep your woodlot as healthy as possible. Many of the things that accomplish this will also help keep water bodies healthy.

Riparian buffers

The key message in this section is to set aside adequately sized buffers or leave strips beside water bodies and streams – to guard water quality, fish and wildlife habitat, and biodiversity values. Your woodlot management plan will need to keep these criteria central. Wherever you have surface water – even small seasonal and / or intermittent streams – you'll need to protect vegetation that shades water. You'll also need to protect mature trees along riparian corridors, and large woody debris in the water and on the shoreline.

Using an ecosystem-based approach which stresses sustainable management harvesting principles *(see sidebar and Resources)* will help ensure this. You'll also reduce erosion problems, weeds, and replanting costs, as well as protect soil, habitat and biodiversity values across your entire woodlot.

If you are planning to log your woodlot using conventional approaches, follow best management practices. *Check Resources.* Our perspective is that it is in your best interest for the long-term health of your property – and probably to sustain long-term revenue – to exceed the guidelines set out in documents such as Conservation and Logging on Private Land in Alberta.

- Clearly flag streams (including seasonal and / or intermittent ones), wetlands, setbacks, and no-harvest areas before any logging begins.
- Do not harvest within riparian buffers; retain them in their natural state.

Resources available to help plan logging include forest cover maps, wildlife habitat rating maps, soil surveys, topographic maps, and aerial photos, as well as extensive guidelines for management practices.

Roads

Minimize the amount of land you use for roads, in order to save money and maintain as much productive forest land as possible. Consider whether lower impact approaches like horse logging, or use of lighter equipment, may work for you.

- Build roads in locations with the least slope, and follow land contours.
- Revegetate after road construction to prevent weed invasion and to stabilize road surface.
- Ensure that excavated soil does not erode into streams. Use water diversion structures to minimize downroad flow. *See Chapter 4.*
- Maintain your access roads and landings; monitor them for signs of slumping or potential erosion, or any potential problems with culverts. When you no longer require a road, deactivate or rehabilitate it.

Other tips

- Work when the ground is dry or frozen. Avoid working during wet conditions when saturated soils can become compacted, resulting in increased potential for erosion.
- Keep landings and slash piles well away from creeks, lakes and low-lying, poorly drained areas. In wet weather, water could pool and sediment could overspill into surface water. And, if you burn the slash, ash could enter surface water.
- ⚠️ **CAUTION: *If you hire contractors to fell trees for you, be very clear about the need to protect water, and procedures for doing so.*** Fines have been levied for infractions damaging streams on private land. Also consider specifying that contractors use lighter rather than heavy equipment, to minimize damage to soils in your woodlot.
- Do not use wetland areas as a dump for harvest debris (tree tops and branches).
- Carry absorbent materials to deal with spills of fuel or oil from equipment and vehicles.

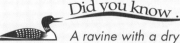

Resources

Caring for the Green Zone: Riparian Areas and Grazing Management. 1995. Adams, Barry and L. Fitch. Cows and Fish Partnership. Lethbridge, Alberta.

The Health of our Water: Toward Sustainable Agriculture in Canada. 2000. Coot, D.R. and L.J. Gregorich, editors. Research Branch, Agriculture and Agri-food Canada.

Conservation and Logging on Private Land in Alberta. Alberta Agriculture, Food and Rural Development

Woodlot Association of Alberta. www.woodlot.org

Whose Shoreline Is It, Anyway?

A number of years after purchasing the resort, we hired surveyors to identify our boundaries. Part of their task was to find the lake's 'natural boundary'. We were surprised when they found that the lake was higher than indicated on the original lot plans, and we'd therefore "lost" some land. This affected setbacks for septic fields and future construction.

Where is our legal property line at the water's edge? What are our rights as waterfront property owners? What are the regulations for building a dock, or accessing water in a creek for drinking? Can we put up a "No Trespassing" sign to stop people walking along the beach? In the past, these actions might all have occurred without much input from government agencies. Now we live in an era of greater awareness.

As we found out when we had our survey carried out, shorelines are dynamic. Whether along a lake, river or stream, shorelines move and change over time. Banks erode, sand and gravel are picked up and re-deposited and water levels fluctuate depending on the season. These processes provide challenges to those who establish the boundaries of water-side land parcels.

 **If your property was last surveyed many years ago, consider hiring a professional surveyor to reassess the shoreline boundary, particularly if you think there has been change through time which may affect the safe setback of a septic field.**

Your Property

Boundaries

As an owner of waterfront property, your property line generally extends to the natural boundary (also frequently called the *bank* or *ordinary high water mark*) of a lake, river or stream, unless you have a municipal or environmental reserve that lies between your property and the water.

The land below the natural boundary is known as the *bed* of the water body and generally belongs to the provincial government (the "Crown"). The shore of a water body is that part of the bed exposed when water levels are below the natural boundary or bank. Beaches, which are dynamic, with sand and pebbles pushed and pulled by waves and ice, generally also lie below the high water mark.

The boundaries of your property are defined first by their legal description (the land title) and by a survey. A copy of the survey plan showing the legal boundary of your property can usually

⚠ CAUTION
Erecting a "Private Property" sign below the High Water Mark on a beach is like putting it up in your local park. Because the land is owned by the Crown, it is available for casual public use.

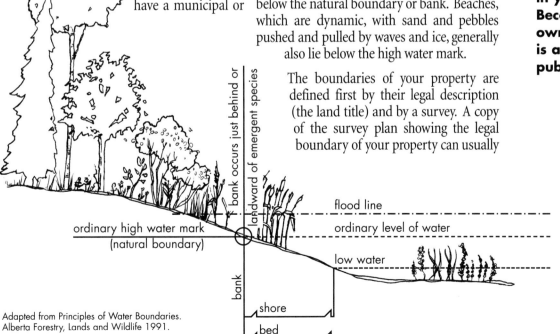

ordinary high water mark
(natural boundary)

bank occurs just behind or landward of emergent species

flood line

ordinary level of water

low water

bank

shore

bed

Adapted from Principles of Water Boundaries.
Alberta Forestry, Lands and Wildlife 1991.

be obtained from the Land Title Office. The natural boundary will appear as a line on the survey plan and reflects the boundary location at the time of the survey. As these boundaries can move over time, the actual location may be different today. You can avoid potential problems by having an Alberta Land Surveyor confirm your property boundaries.

To find the natural boundary, surveyors and other field workers look at things such as changes in soil characteristics (soils above the normal high water mark frequently differ from soils below it). Other indicators include changes in the colour of rock where water has made a mark, and vegetation differences such as the limits of vegetation along a lake's beach.

Use of surface water

If you live on a creek, or have one running through your property with a visible natural boundary, in all likelihood it is considered public property. There are only a few rare instances where a property owner also owns the bed of a creek that goes through his or her property.

Use of surface water (from creeks, rivers and lakes) is regulated by Alberta Environment. Even though you own the property bordering a creek, river or lake, if you wish to install a permanent line to draw water for household use, you may need additional approvals. *See Chapter 6.*

Public access

Because the land below the natural boundary is owned by the province, it is public land, and is therefore available for casual public use. As a waterfront owner, you must permit access across publicly owned land. This means that you can't use fences or other obstructions to keep the public away from the shoreline fronting your property. Such an act would constitute trespass.

Waterfront owners' rights

If you are an owner of waterfront property directly adjacent to a natural water body, you are a riparian land owner. Such landowners enjoy some rights that other landowners do not have but, if your municipality owns the reserve between your property and the water, they are the riparian owner and not you. Riparian rights include:

Right of access

You have the right of access, to and from the water, every point along your waterfront property for the purpose of navigation. This means that no one can prevent you from accessing your land from the water. This right does not include the construction of any moorage or other structure that may occupy the bed of a water body. It also means that you have the right to obtain access – to ask the Crown for permission for any development. The Crown must have good reason to withhold approval.

The right to protect your property from erosion

You may build erosion control structures **on your own land** – that is, above the natural boundary (the ordinary high water mark). However, approval of various agencies, including local government, is usually required to do this. You should also check for any leaseholder regulations, covenants or easements held by a third party which might limit activity. You definitely will need agency approvals if construction below the natural boundary of the water body is necessary for erosion control, and to operate machinery below the high water mark.

The right to acquire land

Sometimes land may build up slowly in front of your property over time through natural processes of deposition (accretion) or exposure by the slow recession of water (reliction). You can apply to have accrued lands registered as part of your land title.

A local Alberta land surveyor will have to confirm that the accretion is due to natural, rather than human causes, and there will be other costs such as legal fees associated with the process of registration.

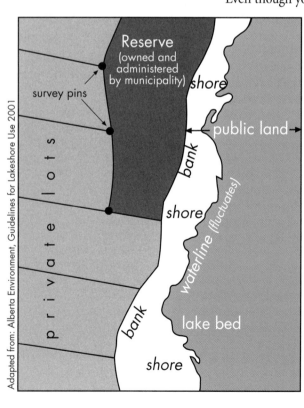

Adapted from: Alberta Environment, Guidelines for Lakeshore Use 2001

Shoreline Development

In Alberta, most of the lands below the high water mark are jointly managed by Alberta Environment, Alberta Sustainable Resource Development (SRD) and Fisheries and Oceans Canada (DFO). To develop or alter the bed and shore of a water body, or place permanent structures on it, you require the authorization of the province and DFO. This includes projects such as pilings, docks, and retaining walls. Improvements or fill placed on the bed and shore without approval are considered to be in trespass and may be subject to penalties.

Public Lands Act tenures

Alberta Sustainable Resource Development and/or Alberta Environment will grant tenures – licences, leases, easements or permits – to individuals, corporations, societies, and local governments who wish to carry out shoreline projects. To receive permission, you (as applicant) must either own the property upland of the area in question, or receive the upland owner's consent. Projects for which you may require a tenure include permanent docks and waterlines; marinas; pipelines; powerlines; moorings; erosion protection works; and community and commercial recreational uses.

Alberta Environment and/or SRD will contact other provincial agencies during the review process to obtain their comments on the implications of your proposal but the applicant is responsible for contacting DFO for additional approvals. Because shoreline areas are so significant – for protecting water quality, and for fish and other wildlife habitat, recreation and industry – there is a lot of interest in development that occurs in these areas. Government takes the view that shoreline development must be managed carefully.

Obtaining approvals

Alberta Environment or SRD are usually the first point of contact for most waterfront residents wishing to carry out alterations on the shoreline. Either department will provide you with the information required for provincial approvals. They will also advise you on contacting the appropriate local municipality,

regional district or First Nations, who will provide comments on land use suitability and compliance with zoning and building bylaws.

As well as addressing the question of working on Crown land, provincial and federal agencies will be reviewing your application from the point of view of environmental impact, particularly the impact on fish habitat.

The Federal Fisheries Act is one of the strongest pieces of legislation that will influence you as a shoreline resident. It legally requires DFO fisheries officers to take action to protect fish habitat.

If you propose activities on your shoreline that might harmfully alter, damage or destroy fish habitat, you are at risk of contravening the federal Fisheries Act. To prevent this (and any resulting fines and difficulties), you will need to receive a written letter of advice from DFO. This letter will indicate that if you follow the terms and conditions outlined, you will be unlikely to damage fish habitat.

Should damage to fish habitat be unavoidable, then a much more detailed, complicated procedure will follow. Environmental screening will be required, referrals made to other agencies, and a formula worked out to identify how you can compensate by creating fish habitat elsewhere. Only DFO can actually authorize habitat destruction, and you will require their authorization before proceeding.

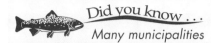

Did you know ...
Many municipalities are helping protect fish habitat by establishing setback and leave strip bylaws to protect shoreline buffers. Check with your local office.

> **"** *I was planning to move a fallen tree from the water off my beach, when a neighbour mentioned that I might need a permit because it's fish habitat. I contacted the local biologist in SRD who gave me permission to shift it enough so it wouldn't interfere with swimming and boating.* **"**
>
> Shoreline resident

Resources

The Law and the Lake: Navigating Alberta's Regulatory Framework. Alberta Lake Management Society. alms.biology.ualberta.ca/Pages-Main/Resources.htm

Guidelines for Lakeshore Use (pamphlet). Alberta Sustainable Resource Development and Alberta Environment.

See Appendix 1 for complete Resources.

⑱ Going the Next Step

*A*fter a few years of chatting with neighbours about how much we enjoyed living on the lake, some of us started to meet to talk about what we could do to help protect it. We take samples to monitor water quality, do a shoreline clean-up in the spring, and write the occasional newsletter to let others know of our activities. We've discovered that there are many people across Alberta who, like us, have taken further steps to care for their shorelines.

tip *Check the relevant box on the Shoreline Action Checklist at the back of this book for information on a shoreline workshop, a home visit, or making a donation to Living by Water.*

Did you know . . .

The Living by Water Project was established in 1997 and has partners across Canada. The project's mission is "working towards healthier human and wildlife habitat across Canada". Check the website: ***www.livingbywater.ca.***

tip *To find out if you live on a waterway which is part of the Canadian Heritage Rivers System, check under "Heritage Rivers"* (Appendix 1)*. There may be special things you can do to help protect this legacy.*

If you want to do more to help protect, conserve, restore and learn more about shorelines, here are some ideas. Remember, small actions can add up to big results!

Shoreline action for your property

- Evaluate your shoreline, using the quiz on Pg 141, to identify elements which might need change to improve its health.
- Use the Shoreline Resident's Action Checklist included with this book as a helpful reminder to identify specific actions you can do. Send the mail-in portion of the checklist to the Living by Water Project and you'll earn a Shoreline Ambassador Certificate. You can also find the Action Checklist on our website.

Working with others

- Join one of the many groups helping to protect and restore shorelines in various ways: a local Fish and Game club, cottager organization, naturalist group, lake stewardship group, streamkeepers, shorekeepers, or wetlandkeepers group.
- If you are a youth leader, incorporate information about healthy shorelines into the work you are doing. Through the Living by Water Project, we are working with both Girl Guides and Scouts Canada to help provide information for young people.
- Work with others to set up a "peer support" network. These may be neighbours, or contacts in other groups, who are interested in learning about protecting shorelines in your area. If there is interest, your group could initiate activities such as

water quality sampling, helping bring environment-friendly products to your area, preparing a natural history brochure of your area, or interviewing elders to learn more about the area's social history.

- Take steps towards long-term protection of the natural features which make your property special. Consider registering a shoreline conservation easement. You may be able to obtain a tax benefit, depending on what steps you take. *See Resources.*

Helping monitor nature

- Help scientists monitor trends along shorelines. For example, join the Canadian Lakes Loon Survey, participate in a program like Project Feeder Watch, Frog Watch, or Ice Watch; or, help carry out a simple wildlife survey. *See Resources.*
- Help a local group conduct regular tests on your water body.

Finding help

There are many resources available through The Living by Water Project to assist individuals and groups.

- Review the resources identified in this book. *See Appendix 1.*
- Check our website. *See sidebar.*
- Consider working with others to bring Living by Water shoreline programs to your area. Two central elements are a workshop for shoreline residents and a shoreline home visit program.
  - The workshop comes as a kit in a box, and is designed to be given by small groups. The material is drawn from this

book and other resources, and expands on several of the topics – healthy shorelines, septic systems, water quality, recreation, erosion and shoreline landscaping.

- The home visit by a trained assessor helps you identify actions and assess potential problems.

● Contact us if you have suggestions or questions. Responses to questions may be posted on the Living by Water Project website.

● Consider working with others to organize a shoreline event or activity in your community – it can be as small or large as you want it! The **Shoreline Event and Activity Manual** can assist you.

Accessing information

In the conversations that we have had with waterfront residents over the past few years while researching this book, frustration with accessing information has been a frequently recurring theme. Although many government agencies and non-government organizations can help you with questions and concerns about your shoreline property, finding the most appropriate one can be challenging. There are several tools available:

The **Blue Pages** of the phone book: These list federal, provincial, and municipal offices. You may need to call representatives from all three levels of government to deal with a question.

The **Yellow Pages** in your phone book: These can guide you in finding businesses like local septic contractors, labs which can test water, and some of the larger non-government agencies. If you live in a smaller community, you will likely need to look at the Yellow Pages for the largest centre near you.

Local community resource directories These are usually an excellent way to find groups and organizations which aren't in the phone book. These directories are often available through a local service agency, libraries, or Chamber of Commerce.

Internet You can use a "search engine" and enter the key words which describe your problem (be sure also to enter "Alberta" if you want to limit your search to agencies in the province). You'll get a list of sites which match your search criteria, with the best matches first. Many government agencies are putting their publications on their websites, as a way of providing service during times of reduced budgets.

Government agencies Government officials are there to help you with information and resources. You can avoid unnecessary fines or penalties if you "do it right" the first time! Always ask for clarification if you do not understand what you are being told. If the agency you call is not able to answer your question, ask them for suggestions on who you should call. Ask if they can provide you with a contact name and phone number.

Non-government organizations In almost every community there is a range of non-government organizations dedicated to environmental stewardship, conservation, helping ratepayers, and local community service. Many of these have individual members experienced in working with government organizations, who will be able to help you with information and resources to solve specific problems.

Conclusion

Our shorelines buffer us from the forces of nature, and act as a line of defence in protecting water quality. They're also a ribbon of life fundamental to our well-being. We, as shoreline residents, are their guardians – to protect our own properties, water quality, and fish and other wildlife. We have perhaps the most direct influence on this ribbon of life.

We have a choice: if we each make small changes, we can gradually help our shorelines return to conditions where they can do their work better for us. We can also influence our shoreline neighbours and other members of the community. We can be leaders, demonstrating that it is possible to live cooperatively with nature in critical shoreline zones.

> *Because we love the lake and its wildlife so much, we placed a voluntary conservation easement on our shoreline to help protect it for our children. We worked with a local non-government organization to make this happen.*
>
> Sarah and Clive

tip *You can avoid survey costs when registering a shoreline conservation easement by defining the land to be protected as a certain setback – for example, 15 m (50 ft) – from the high water line.*

tip *Toll-free numbers are available to help you track down the government department which can help you. Federal agencies: 1-800-622-6232 or 1-800-667-3355 Provincial agencies: 310-0000*

Resources

Community Stewardship: A Guide to Establishing Your Own Group. Environment Canada and Fisheries and Oceans Canada.

For the Love of Alberta: Ways to Save Your Natural Heritage. 1998. Curthoys, Patricia Lesley. Federation of Alberta Naturalists. Edmonton, Alberta.

Stewardship Canada. www.stewardshipcanada.ca
See Appendix 1 for complete Resources.

Contacts and Resources

This appendix lists contact information for a variety of topics. References *(Pg 142)* and Resources (at the end of some chapters) also provide contact information and sources of help.

What?	Who?	Where?
Agricultural questions (livestock, fencing, waste management, crops)	Alberta Agriculture, Food and Rural Development	310-0000 www.agric.gov.ab.ca
Algal blooms	Local Health Unit – Environmental Health Officer	Blue Pages
	Health Canada	http://www.hc-sc.gc.ca/ehp/ehd/catalogue/general/iyh/algea.htm
Approvals (work above or below high water mark)	Alberta Environment and/or Sustainable Resource Development (SRD)	310-0000
	Local municipal office	Blue pages
	Fisheries and Oceans Canada (DFO)	1-800-667-3665
Aquifers (maps, etc.)	Alberta Environment	310-0000 www3.gov.ab.ca/env
Bats	Bat Conservation International	www.batcon.org
	Bats in Alberta	www3.gov.ab.ca/srd/fw/bats/
Boating		
safety	Boating Safety Infoline	1-800-267-6687 www.ccg-gcc.gc.ca/obs-bsn/sbg-gsn/main_e.htm
speed restrictions, regulations	Canadian Coast Guard – No Discharge Zones – Boating restriction regulations	www.ccg-gcc.gc.ca/
green boating	Canadian Power and Sail Squadrons	1-800-268-3579 or 1-800-808-BOAT www.cps-ecp.ca
Building regulations, bylaws	Municipal office	Blue pages
Burning permit (for yard waste)	Local municipality	Blue pages
fire ban information	SRD	1-866-FYI-FIRE (394-3473)
Business reputation	Better Business Bureau	www.canadiancouncilbbb.ca
	Local Chamber of Commerce	Blue pages
Conservation agreements and easements	Nature Conservancy of Canada	(403) 294-7064
	Environmental Law Centre	1-800-661-4238
ecological gifts	Canadian Wildlife Service	(780) 951-8673 www.cws-scf.ec.gc.ca/ecogifts
Dams	*See Reservoirs and Dams*	
Docks (approvals, etc.)	Alberta Environment and/or SRD	310-0000
	DFO	1-800-667-3355
EMERGENCY	Local emergency services	911 or local emergency number
preparedness	Alberta Municipal Affairs, Disaster Services	310-0000 www3.gov.ab.ca/ma/ds/
Erosion problems	Alberta Environment	310-0000
	Local municipality	Blue pages
	Specialized professional *(see Chapter 8)*	Yellow pages or through reference from local group

What?	Who?	Where?
Fire reporting	Local emergency services	911 or local emergency number
forest fires	Local forestry office	(780) 427-FIRE (3473) or #FIRE on the Telus Mobility Network
Fish habitat	SRD	310-0000 www3.gov.ab.ca
	Local Fish and Wildlife Office	Blue Pages
	DFO	1-800-667-3355 www.dfo-mpo.gc.ca/habitat/home_e.htm
Fishing regulations	SRD – Local Fish and Wildlife Office	310-0000 or Blue Pages
Flood protection	Alberta Environment	310-0000
	Municipal Office	Blue pages
	Alberta Municipal Affairs	www3.gov.ab.ca/ma/ds/fs_faqs.cfm
	Emergency Preparedness Canada	1-800-663-3456 http://www.ocipep-bpiepc.gc.ca
Gardening	NatureScape Alberta (publ.)	www.naturescape.ab.ca
	Organic Landscape Alliance	www.organiclandscape.org/factsheets.htm
	Go for Green	www.goforgreen.ca/gardening
	Landscape Alberta Nursery Trades Association	www.landscape-alberta.com
	Local composting program	Municipal government (blue pages)
	Elora Centre for Environmental Excellence	www.ecee.on.ca/pesticidefree.htm
	Devonian Botanic Garden	www.discoveredmonton.com/devonian
Hazardous material disposal (paint, flammables, gasoline, and pesticides)	Alberta Environment	310-0000 www3.gov.ab.ca/env
Health concerns	Local Health Unit – Environ. Health Officer	Blue pages
(water quality, hot tubs, sewage disposal)	Alberta Municipal Affairs	310-0000
Heritage Rivers	Canadian Heritage Rivers System	www.chrs.ca/Main_e.htm
High water mark, locating	Municipal office	Blue pages
	SRD	310-0000 www3.gov.ab.ca
	DFO	1-800-667-3355
	Registered land surveyor	Yellow pages
Invasive species		
removal	Alberta Agriculture, Food and Rural Development	310-0000 www.agric.gov.ab.ca
	DFO	1-800-667-3355
identification	Alberta Native Plant Council	www.anpc.ab.ca
	Canadian Wildlife Service	www.cws-scf.ec.gc.ca
purple loosestrife	Ducks Unlimited	www.ducks.ca/purple/faq/
Lake information	Alberta Water Management Society	www.alms.ca
	Alberta Environment	310-0000 www3.gov.ab.ca/env
Lighting	International Dark-Sky Association	www.darksky.org/ida/index.html
	Sensible Shoreland Lighting (publ.)	www.uwsp.edu/cnr/uwexlakes/publications/lighting.pdf
		See References

What?	Who?	Where?
Native plants	Alberta Native Plant Council	www.anpc.ab.ca
	Plant hardiness zones	http://sis.agr.gc.ca/cansis/nsdb/climate/hardiness/intro.html
	Devonian Botanic Gardens	www.discoveredmonton.com/devonian
	Appendix 2	
Naturalists clubs	Federation of Alberta Naturalists	(780) 427-8124 www.fanweb.ca
Nature Watch (ice, frogs, birds, plants)	Canadian Nature Federation	www.cnf.ca/watch.html
	Feeder Watch	www.cnf.ca/educate/edu_involv_feeder.html
	Butterfly Survey	www.cwf-fcf.org/surveys/butter.htm
	Loon Watch – Canadian Lakes Loon Survey – Bird Studies Canada	www.bsc-eoc.org/cllsmain.htm
Nest boxes	Ducks Unlimited Canada	www.ducks.ca/nestboxes/duckbox.pdf
	Nestboxes for Alberta Birds (publ.)	Local Bookstore
	Local Naturalists Club or Nature Centre	Local Contact Information
Pesticide-free gardening	Elora Centre for Environmental Excellence	www.ecee.on.ca/pesticide_free.htm
	Organic Landscape Alliance	www.organiclandscape.org/factsheets.htm
	The Garden Institute	(780) 461-9958 www.mkids.com/Garden/
Poaching	Report a Poacher	1-800-642-3800
Pollution		www.scorecard.org/pollutionwatch/
spills on the water	*See Spills*	
pollution on land	Alberta Environment	310-0000
Recycling	Alberta Environment	310-0000 www3.gov.ab.ca/env
	Local Municipality	Blue Pages
Registering your group as a society	Alberta Corporate Affairs	310-0000 www3.gov.ab.ca
Reservoirs and dams	Alberta Environment	310-0000 www3.gov.ab.ca/env
River data	Environment Canada	www.scitech.pyr.ec.gc.ca/water/Map.asp
	Alberta Environment	www3.gov.ab.ca/env
Septic systems	Local Health Unit – Environmental Health Officer	Blue pages
	Alberta Municipal Affairs	310-0000 www.gov.ab.ca
	University of Minnesota – Septic System Owner's Guide	www.extension.umn.edu/distribution/naturalresources/DD6583.html
Shoreline monitoring and enhancement	DFO	1-800-667-3355
	Alberta Lake Management Society	www.alms.ca/
	Vincent Lake Working Group	www.healthyshorelines.com
	Cows and Fish Program	Alberta Riparian Habitat Management Program www.cowsandfish.org
Shoreline restoration information	Shoreland Restoration home page	www.uwex.edu/ces/shoreland
	Minnesota Shoreland Management Resource Guide	www.shorelandmanagement.org

What?	Who?	Where?
Soil surveys	Alberta Agriculture, Food and Rural Development	310-0000
Spills (fuel, oil)	Canadian Coast Guard	1-800-889-8852 or VHF 16
	Alberta Environment	310-0000
Stewardship	Stewardship Canada	www.stewardshipcanada.ca
	Land Stewardship Resource Centre	www.landstewardship.org
Swimming		
safety	Canadian Red Cross	www.redcross.ca/english/watersafety
platforms (approvals)	Canadian Coast Guard – navigable waters	www.ccg-gcc.gc.ca/cen-arc/home-accuil_e.htm
Toxic alternatives	Georgia Strait Alliance	www.georgiastrait.org
Volunteering		
water testing on surface water shoreline monitoring	Alberta Lake Watch	http://alms.biology.ualberta.ca/PagesMain/LakeWatch.htm
Water		
general	Alberta Environment	310-0000 www3.gov.ab.ca/env
	Environment Canada	www.ec.gc.ca/water
conservation	Water wiser	www.waterwiser.org/
	Alberta Environment	310-0000 www3.gov.ab.ca/env
rights	Alberta Lake Management Society	www.alms.ca
quality	Local Health Unit – Environmental Health Officer	Blue pages
surface water	Alberta Environment	310-0000 www3.gov.ab.ca/env
	Alberta Agriculture, Food and Rural Development	310-0000 www.agric/gov.ab.ca
wells	Alberta Agriculture, Food and Rural Development	310-0000 www.agric/gov.ab.ca
working in and around	Alberta Environment and/or SRD	310-0000
	DFO	1-800-667-3355 www.dfo-mpo.gc.ca
	Alberta Conservation Association	1-877-969-9091
Watershed planning and restoration	North Saskatchewan Water Alliance	(780) 496-3474 www.nswa.ab.ca
	Partners for the Saskatchewan River Basin	(780) 665-6887 1-800-567-8007 www.saskriverbasin.ca
	Bow River Basin Council	(403) 254-3419 www.brbc.ab.ca
	Oldman River Basin Water Quality Initiative	(403) 381-5880 www.oldmanbasin.org
Wetlands information/ education	Wetkit: tools for working with wetlands	www.wetkit.net
	Ducks Unlimited	Local Contact Information; www.ducks.ca
Wildlife habitat protection and enhancement	DFO-Habitat and Enhancement Br.	1-800-667-3355 www.dfo-mpo.gc.ca
	NatureScape Alberta (publ.)	www.naturescape.ab.ca
	SRD	310-0000 www3.gov.ab.ca
	Canadian Wildlife Service	www.cws-scf.ec.gc.ca
	See also listings under Nature Watch, Nest Boxes	
Wildlife, injured	SRD Conservation Officer	Blue pages; www3.gov.ab.ca
	Local Wildlife Rehabilitation Centre	local contact information
	Local Veterinarian	Yellow Pages

Native Plant Species

The plants on this list are widely available across the province; local native plant nurseries may be able to suggest additional suitable species. We recommend planting nursery grown stock except where noted, although propagation is often possible using a variety of techniques. Conifers are best purchased as small trees (plugs) from local forestry nurseries. **CAUTION:** Always check with local nurseries, resource people such as naturalists and web sites to ensure that the plants you have selected are appropriate for your area and site conditions. Suitable regions for each plant are noted in the chart.

Trees	shore stabilization	can be aggressive	sun	part shade	shade	dry	some moisture	wet	maximum height (metres)	comments *(also see notes Pg 138)*
River Alder *(Alnus incana or A. tenuifolia)*			●	●	●		●		8	fast-growing, nitrogen fixing, often grows in clumps, boreal forest, parkland and mountains
Paper or White Birch *(Betula papyrifera)*			●				●		30	fast-growing, yellow fall leaves, white peeling bark, not drought tolerant, boreal forest, parkland and mountains
Tamarack *(Larix laricina)*			●	●			●	●	15	fine needles which turn yellow and drop in fall, boreal forest
White Spruce *(Picea glauca)*			●	●	●		●		40	slow growing, shade-tolerant, boreal forest, parkland and mountains
Jack Pine *(Pinus banksiana)*	●		●			●	●		20	fast growing, sandy soils, boreal forest and parkland
Lodgepole Pine *(Pinus contorta)*	●		●			●	●		30	excellent with ground covers, adaptable to many sites, fast growing, boreal forest and foothills
Trembling Aspen *(Populus tremuloides)*	●	●	●				●		30	fast-growing, yellow fall leaves, forms dense groves by suckering, likes sandy or gravelly soils, throughout Alberta
Balsam Poplar *(Populus balsamifera)*	●		●				●	●	25	very fast-growing, fragrant leaves, shallow-rooted, short-lived, trees will re-sprout when cut, valuable in restoring flooded lands or other wet habitat, propagate from cuttings, throughout Alberta

Shrubs and Shrubby Trees

	shore stabilization	can be aggressive	sun	part shade	shade	dry	some moisture	wet	maximum height (metres)	comments
Green Alder *(Alnus crispa)*			●	●	●		●	●	3	sandy soils, roots fix nitrogen, disturbed sites and bare areas, high flood and snow resistance, boreal forest, parkland and mountains
Saskatoon, Serviceberry *(Amelanchier alnifolia)*	●		●	●	●	●	●		6	showy white flowers, edible fruit, upright, spreading, good for dry sites, throughout Alberta
Bog Birch *(Betula glandulosa)*			●	●	●			●	2	small leaves, good for wet sites, boreal forest and mountains
Water Birch *(Betula occidentalis)*			●	●	●		●	●	10	tall shrub with glossy brown bark, prairie, parkland and mountains
Dwarf Birch *(Betula pumila glandulifera)*			●	●	●			●	2	slender shrub, swamps and bogs, boreal forest, parkland and mountains
Red-Osier Dogwood *(Cornus stolonifera or sericea)*	●		●	●			●	●	3	showy red twigs, white flowers and berries, fast-growing, good erosion control, propagate from cuttings, throughout Alberta
Beaked Hazelnut *(Corylus cornuta)*			●	●			●		3	yellow autumn colour, edible nuts, good stream-side plant but intolerant of saturated soil, boreal forest and parkland
Douglas Hawthorn *(Crataegus douglasii)*			●	●			●		5	shrub or small tree, yellow fall foliage, thorns, dark purple fruit attracts birds, southern prairie
Round Hawthorn *(Crataegus rotundifolia)*			●	●			●		5	shrub or small tree, yellow fall foliage, thorns, red or orange fruit attracts birds, prairie and parkland
Silver-berry, Wolf Willow *(Elaeagnus commutata)*	●	●	●			●	●		4	silver foliage, yellow flowers, good erosion control, prairie and parkland
Creeping Juniper *(Juniperus horizontalis)*	●		●			●			0.3	good ground cover, dry banks and sandy hillsides, good erosion control, prairie, parkland and mountains

	shore stabilization	can be aggressive	sun	part shade	shade	dry	some moisture	wet	maximum height (metres)	comments (also see notes Pg 138)
Twining Honeysuckle (*Lonicera dioica*)			●	●	●		●		1	twining woody vine, yellow flowers, red fruits, open woods, boreal forest, parkland and mountains
Bracted Honeysuckle (*Lonicera involucrata*)			●	●	●		●	●	3	fast-growing erect shrub, likes moist forest, clearings, stream sides, swamps, boreal forest, parkland and mountains
Shrubby Cinquefoil (*Potentilla fruticosa*)	●		●	●		●	●		1.5	showy yellow flowers, good for dry open sites, easily roots from cuttings, mountains, prairie and parkland
Pin Cherry (*Prunus pensylvanica*)			●	●			●		6	white flowers, fruit attractive to birds, thickets and open woods, throughout Alberta
Choke Cherry (*Prunus virginiana*)			●	●			●	●	5	clusters of white flowers, purple fruit, dry woods and exposed sites, throughout Alberta
Wild Black Currant (*Ribes americanum*)			●	●			●	●	1	edible berries, streambanks and woods, parkland
Golden Currant (*Ribes aureum*)			●	●		●	●		2	red or black fruit, banks and rocky slopes, prairie
Black Gooseberry (*Ribes lacustre*)			●	●			●	●	1	black berries, bristles can irritate some people, moist woods and streambanks, boreal forest and mountains
Wild Gooseberry (*Ribes oxyacanthoides*)			●	●			●	●	1.5	edible berries, open woods and exposed sites, bristles, throughout Alberta
Wild Red Currant (*Ribes triste*)			●	●			●	●	1	red berries, moist woods and swamps, boreal forest and parkland
Prickly Rose (*Rosa acicularis*)			●				●		2	pink flowers and red hips, poor erosion control, needs water for establishment, parkland, boreal forest and mountains
Common Wild Rose (*Rosa woodsii*)			●	●			●		1.5	pink flowers and red hips, poor erosion control, needs water for establishment, throughout Alberta
Wild Red Raspberry (*Rubus idaeus*)			●	●	●		●		2	edible red fruit, spreads easily, spiny, thickets and clearings, throughout Alberta
Beaked Willow (*Salix bebbiana*)	●		●	●				●	5	fast-growing, likes to be near water, new growth is showy yellow, tolerates flooding, propagates from cuttings, good erosion control, throughout Alberta
Pussy Willow (*Salix discolor*)	●		●	●			●		11	stream banks, thickets around sloughs, fast-growing, propagates from cuttings, throughout Alberta
Sandbar Willow (*Salix exigua*)	●		●	●			●	●	4	dense, fast-growing, tolerates flooding, propagates from cuttings, throughout Alberta
Shining Willow (*Salix lasiandra*)	●		●	●			●	●	9	lake and slough margins, flood plains, propagates from cuttings, throughout Alberta
Meadow Willow (*Salix petiolaris*)	●		●	●			●	●	5	meadows and lakeshores, propagates from cuttings, throughout Alberta
Scouler's Willow (*Salix scouleriana*)	●		●	●			●	●	7	fast-growing, tolerates flooding, drought-tolerant, propagates from cuttings, boreal forest and mountains
Red Elderberry (*Sambucus racemosa*)		●	●	●			●		6	white flower clusters, showy red fruit, spreads easily, berries edible when cooked, moist woods, eastern boreal forest
Thorny Buffalo-berry (*Shepherdia argentea*)	●		●	●			●	●	6	silver foliage, thorns, small yellow flowers and silvery fruit, good erosion control, prairie and parkland
Canadian Buffalo-berry (*Shepherdia canadensis*)	●		●	●		●	●		3	open woods and river banks, spreading shrub, red-berries, good erosion control, boreal forest, parkland and mountains
Narrow-leaved Meadow Sweet (*Spiraea alba*)			●	●			●	●	2	white flowers, wet meadows and shores, parkland and boreal forest

	shore stabilization	can be aggressive	sun	part shade	shade	dry	some moisture	wet	maximum height (metres)	comments (also see notes Pg 138)
Snowberry (*Symphoricarpos albus*)	●		●	●	●	●	●	●	1	dense thickets, suckers readily, open woods and slopes, parkland and boreal forest
Buckbrush (*Symphoricarpos occidentalis*)	●		●	●		●	●		1	open woods and prairie slopes, good erosion control, parkland and prairie
Low-bush Cranberry (*Viburnum edule*)			●	●	●		●	●	2	white flowers, red berries, moist woods, parkland, boreal forest and mountains
High-bush Cranberry (*Viburnum opulus*)			●	●			●	●	4	showy white flowers, red berries, moist woods, parkland

Ground Covers, Wetland Plants and Herbaceous Perennials

WILDFLOWERS – The plants listed here are good choices for establishing your buffer. Many spread easily but may need some management. If you want to increase the variety of plants in your buffer, check the ANPC website (see notes) for a full list of native plants and sources.

	shore stabilization	can be aggressive	sun	part shade	shade	dry	some moisture	wet	maximum height (metres)	comments (also see notes Pg 138)
Common Yarrow (*Achillea millefolium*)	●	●	●	●		●	●	●	0.8	grasslands, open woods, white flowers, spreads easily, throughout Alberta
Canada Anemone (*Anemone canadensis*)		●	●	●	●		●		0.7	white flowers, woodlands, spreads easily, throughout Alberta
Pasture Sagewort (*Artemisia frigida*)		●	●	●		●			0.4	grasslands, open areas, silver foliage, spreads easily, prairie, parkland and mountains
Bearberry (*Arctostaphylos uva-ursi*)			●			●	●		1	good ground cover, small pink flowers and red berries, parkland, boreal forest and mountains
Tufted White Prairie Aster (*Aster ericoides*)		●	●	●			●		0.8	dry grasslands, white flowers, spreads easily, prairie and parkland
Smooth Aster (*Aster laevis*)			●	●	●		●		1	moist grasslands and open woods, pink to purple flowers, prairie, parkland and mountains
Two-grooved Milk Vetch (*Astragalus bisulcatus*)			●	●			●		1	purple flowers, grasslands, coulees, prairie and parkland
Harebell (*Campanula rotundifolia*)			●	●		●	●		0.4	meadows, hillsides and open woods, blue flowers, throughout Alberta
Bunchberry (*Cornus canadensis*)			●	●	●		●		0.2	white flowers, red berries, open woods, parkland, boreal forest and mountains
Yellow Mountain Avens (*Dryas drummondii*)	●		●			●	●		0.2	good ground cover, gravel slopes, riverbars, inconspicuous yellow flowers, attractive seedheads, mountains and foothills
Smooth Fleabane (*Erigeron glabellus*)			●				●		0.5	moist woods and grasslands, pink flowers, throughout Alberta
Wild Strawberry (*Fragaria virginiana*)		●	●	●			●		0.1	small edible red fruit, meadows and open woods, spreads easily, good ground cover, throughout Alberta
Blanket Flower (*Gaillardia aristata*)			●	●		●	●		0.6	woodlands and prairie valleys, showy yellow/red flowers, prairie, parkland and mountains
Northern Bedstraw (*Gallium boreale*)		●	●	●	●		●		0.6	woodlands and moist grasslands, spreads easily, small white flowers, throughout Alberta
Richardson's Alumroot (*Heuchera richardsonii*)			●	●			●	●	0.4	sandy ground, rocky shores, moist areas, parkland, prairie and mountains
Cream-coloured Pea Vine (*Lathyrus ochroleucus*)	●		●	●			●	●	1	moist woods and clearings, climbing, pale yellow flowers, boreal forest, parkland and mountains
Wild Flax (*Linum lewisii*)			●	●		●	●		0.7	grasslands, blue flowers, spreads easily, prairie and parkland
Wild Mint (*Mentha arvense*)		●	●	●	●		●	●	0.5	moist to wet woods and meadows, scented leaves, spreads easily, throughout Alberta

Native Plant Species

	shore stabilization	can be aggressive	sun	part shade	shade	dry	some moisture	wet	maximum height (metres)	comments (also see notes Pg 138)
Tall Lungwort (*Mertensia paniculata*)			●	●	●		●	●	0.8	moist woods and streambanks, blue flowers, boreal forest, parkland and mountains
Bergamot (*Monarda fistulosa*)		●	●	●	●			●	0.7	woods, fields and shady banks, purple flowers, spreads easily, prairie and parkland
Slender Blue Beard-tongue (*Penstemon procerus*)		●	●	●			●	●	0.4	moist meadows, slough margins and woods, blue flowers, spreads easily, prairie, parkland and mountains
Purple Prairie Clover (*Petalostemon purpureum*)			●			●	●		0.8	grasslands, eroded slopes and banks, purple flowers, prairie
Graceful Cinquefoil (*Potentilla gracilis*)			●	●			●		0.7	grasslands and woods, trailing ground cover, yellow flowers, prairie, parkland and boreal forest
Star-flowered Solomon's Seal (*Smilacina stellata*)	●		●	●			●	●	0.6	open woods and moist shores, white flowers, spreads easily, throughout Alberta
Canada Goldenrod (*Solidago canadensis*)	●		●	●			●	●	1	woods and meadows, showy yellow flowers, spreads easily, throughout Alberta
Veiny Meadow-rue (*Thalictrum venulosum*)	●		●	●	●		●	●	0.9	woods and thickets, spreads easily, throughout Alberta
Western Canada Violet (*Viola canadensis*)	●		●	●	●		●	●	0.4	moist woods and meadows, white flowers, spreads easily, throughout Alberta

Grasses and Sedges

	shore stabilization	can be aggressive	sun	part shade	shade	dry	some moisture	wet	maximum height (metres)	comments
Wheat Grass (*Agropyron spp.*)	●		●	●		●	●	●	0.5-1.5	excellent erosion control, species that can withstand drought, flood and alkaline soils across Alberta, avoid invasive, non-native species
Reed Grass (*Calamagrostis spp.*)	●	●	●	●			●	●	0.5-1.5	good erosion control but can be aggressive, throughout Alberta
Sedge (*Carex spp.*)	●		●	●	●	●	●	●	0.3–1	wide variety of species, good for wet and drier shores
Tufted Hairgrass (*Deschampsia cespitosa*)	●		●	●			●	●	1.2	variety of soil types, excellent erosion control, forms attractive clumps, prairie, parkland and mountains
Salt Grass (*Distichlis stricta*)	●		●	●			●	●	0.4	saline areas, excellent erosion control, prairie and parkland
June Grass (*Koeleria cristata*)	●		●	●		●	●		0.5	grasslands and openings, good erosion control, throughout Alberta
Indian Rice Grass (*Oryzopsis hymenoides*)	●		●	●		●			0.7	dunes and dry banks, excellent erosion control, prairie
Common Reed Grass (*Phragmites communis*)			●	●			●	●	3	marshes, shorelines, forms large clumps, parkland and boreal forest
Needle Grass (*Stipa spp.*)	●		●	●		●	●			grasslands and open areas, prairie, parkland and mountains

Wetland Plants

	shore stabilization	can be aggressive	sun	part shade	shade	dry	some moisture	wet	maximum height (metres)	comments
Marsh Marigold (*Caltha palustris*)			●	●				●	0.6	yellow flowers, wet meadows and shores, parkland and boreal forest
Coontail (*Ceratophyllum demersum*)			●					●	1.5	shallow water in ponds, lakes and ditches throughout Alberta
Baltic Rush (*Juncus balticus*)	●		●					●	0.6	saline and sandy shores, meadows and marshes, throughout Alberta
Pond Lily (*Nuphar variegatum*)			●					●	0.3	yellow flowers, shallow water, floating leaves, parkland and boreal forest

	shore stabilization	can be aggressive	sun	part shade	shade	dry	some moisture	wet	maximum height (metres)	comments (also see notes below)
Smartweed (*Polygonum spp*)			●					●	1	shallow water in ponds, lakes, ditches and muddy shores throughout Alberta, food for moose, muskrats and beavers
Pondweed (*Potamogeton spp*)			●					●	0.3	shallow water in ponds and lakes, important food for birds and mammals
Crowfoot (*Ranunculus spp.*)		●	●					●	0.1	shallow water, white or yellow flowers
Hardstem Bulrush (*Scirpus acutus*)			●					●	2	wetlands and lakeshores throughout Alberta
Common Great Bulrush (*Scirpus validus*)			●					●	2.5	wetlands and lakeshores throughout Alberta, salt-tolerant
Cattail (*Typha latifolia*)	●		●					●	2	slow water, wetlands and ditches, throughout Alberta
Arrowhead (*Sagittaria cuneata*)			●					●	0.5	showy, white flowers, marshes, ditches, muddy shores, throughout Alberta

Notes to Native Plant List

Shore stabilization: These species help stabilize an eroding bank.

Can be aggressive: These species spread easily and may need management.

Grass mixes for riparian revegetation can be purchased from various sources. Take care that any seed mix you buy has a good balance of species and that it does not contain seeds of invasive species (*see below*); avoid seed mixes labelled "Ground Cover" or "Forage" for this reason.

For further information, consult reference books and plant guides, Appendix 1, and the following:

Alberta Native Plant Council Species Supplier Index. Updated 1999. www.anpc.ab.ca

A Guide to Using Native Plants on Disturbed Lands. 1996. Alberta Agriculture, Food and Rural Development.

Alien Invasive Plant Species

Below is a partial list of alien invasive plants of greatest concern for Alberta. There may be additional plants that are problematic in your specific area; check with local experts and resource agency staff such as provincial and federal agrologists and local naturalists. Also check the Rogue's Gallery of Invasive Non-native Plants on the Alberta Native Plant Council web site (www.anpc.ab.ca).

Plants will often become invasive only if particular climatic and site conditions are met. However, a plant may grow in a wider range of conditions than previously observed, and the current effects of climate change may actually increase the range of some plants so it is best to err on the side of caution. For further information, *see Appendix 1*.

(*Agropyron pectiniforme or cristatum*) – Crested Wheatgrass

(*Agropyron repens*) – Quackgrass

(*Bromus inermis*) – Smooth Brome

(*Bromus tectorum*) – Cheatgrass

(*Caragana arborescens*) – Caragana

(*Chrysanthemum leucanthemum*) – Ox-eye Daisy

(*Cirsium arvense*) – Canada Thistle

(*Euphorbia esula*) – Leafy Spurge

(*Kochia scoparia*) – Summer Cypress, Burning Bush

(*Linaria dalmatica & L. vulgaris*) – Toadflax

(*Lythrum salicaria*) – Purple Loosestrife

(*Melilotus sp.*) – Sweetclover

(*Phleum pratense*) – Timothy

(*Poa pratensis*) – Kentucky Bluegrass

Special Considerations for Sensitive Wildlife

Depending on where you live, you may find yourself sharing your lake or wetland with a variety of wildlife that is particularly sensitive to human disturbance. Actions such as planting a grass lawn, removing aquatic plants, or using motorized vehicles too close to the shore, alter native habitat necessary for wildlife survival. Nesting sites may be lost or disturbed, nestlings abandoned, food sources destroyed and pests introduced, all adding stress to sensitive wildlife.

Being aware of sensitive wildlife along your shoreline allows you to choose actions which will help protect them while also increasing your own enjoyment. Simple things, such as using non-motorized boats so that you don't flood nests with waves from the wake, or protecting healthy shoreline buffers to maintain habitat, will benefit the wildlife along your shore.

On many southern prairie lakes you can still find nesting Piping Plovers while in northwestern Alberta there are nesting Trumpeter Swans. Many lakes support colonies of breeding grebes, herons, or pelicans. Shorelines are also important hunting grounds for garter snakes, salamanders and toads. All of these species are particularly sensitive to human disturbance; take special care when living side-by-side with them.

Enhancing habitat for sensitive species

	Maintain a dense zone of emergent vegetation	Increase shoreline buffer zone	Avoid docks	Leave beach area undisturbed	Use non-motorized boats	Don't disturb nest sites	Keep pets and live-stock off the shore	Keep all vehicles off the shore
Birds								
Common Loon	•	•	•		•	•	•	•
Western Grebe	•	•	•		•	•	•	•
Horned Grebe	•	•	•		•	•	•	•
Trumpeter Swan	•	•	•		•	•	•	•
Piping Plover		•		•		•	•	•
Pelican						•	•	•
Herons	•	•				•	•	•
Reptiles and Amphibians								
Garter Snake		•		•			•	•
Tiger Salamander		•		•			•	•
Canadian and Western Toad		•		•			•	•
Leopard frog		•		•			•	•

Shoreline Purchaser Checklist

If you are considering a purchase of shoreline property, we recommend that you ask the seller the following questions in addition to those in any Alberta Property Disclosure Statements. This list is provided as a guide only. We cannot guarantee that it covers all situations. You may wish to request the seller to sign this page, and refer to it in any offer of purchase you make. *See also entry in Index for Purchasing Tips.*

yes · no · don't know · not applicable

water supply *See Chapter 6*
Is the property serviced by a private well? ☐ ☐ ☐ ☐
If YES:
  Are there any water quality problems? ☐ ☐ ☐ ☐
  Do you have records of water quality tests? ☐ ☐ ☐ ☐
  Do you have the well records? ☐ ☐ ☐ ☐
  Is the well properly sealed? ☐ ☐ ☐ ☐
  Is there an adequate and reliable rate of flow? ☐ ☐ ☐ ☐
  Is there an underground storage cistern? ☐ ☐ ☐ ☐
  Has the well ever run dry? ☐ ☐ ☐ ☐
Does the property obtain its water from a surface supply? ☐ ☐ ☐ ☐
If YES:
  Does it have a permanent water line? ☐ ☐ ☐ ☐
  Is there a licence of occupation for the system? ☐ ☐ ☐ ☐
  Is the licence current and will it be transferred with sale of the property? ☐ ☐ ☐ ☐
  Is there a water treatment system in place? ☐ ☐ ☐ ☐
  Is there an underground storage cistern? ☐ ☐ ☐ ☐

septic system *See Chapter 5*
Are the premises connected to a public sanitary sewer system? ☐ ☐ ☐ ☐
If NO:
  Is a sewer system planned in the next three years? ☐ ☐ ☐ ☐
  Is the property system service by a tank and field septic system or lagoon? ☐ ☐ ☐ ☐
  If YES:
  Is there a permit for the system? ☐ ☐ ☐ ☐
  Is the septic field over 15 m (50 ft) from a well? *See Pg 37.* ☐ ☐ ☐ ☐
  Is the septic field over 90 m (300 ft) from surface water? (unless there is a principle building between the field and the water) ☐ ☐ ☐ ☐
  Has the tank been pumped in the last 3 years? ☐ ☐ ☐ ☐
  Is the tank of an adequate size for the dwellings(s)? ☐ ☐ ☐ ☐
  Is there a second drain field, or space for it? ☐ ☐ ☐ ☐
  Is it an "alternative" or "engineered" septic system? ☐ ☐ ☐ ☐
  If NO:
  Is the septic system connected to a holding tank and how often does the tank need pumping? ☐ ☐ ☐ ☐

plumbing
Is the plumbing system built for year-round use? ☐ ☐ ☐ ☐

underground storage tanks
Are there any underground storage tanks for oil, aviation fuel, gasoline or other hazardous liquids on the property? ☐ ☐ ☐ ☐

property boundaries *See Chapter 17*
Are there any special zoning regulations, setbacks, shoreline protection bylaws or environmental reserves? ☐ ☐ ☐ ☐
Are there any adjoining road allowances for public water access, including any old shoreline road allowances? ☐ ☐ ☐ ☐
Are there any easements (including conservation easements) or restrictive covenants registered against the property? ☐ ☐ ☐ ☐
Are you aware of any encroachments, unregistered easements or unregistered rights-of-way? ☐ ☐ ☐ ☐
Does anyone have unregistered access across the property? ☐ ☐ ☐ ☐

erosion *See Chapter 8*
Are there any runoff control measures (culverts, waterbars) in place? ☐ ☐ ☐ ☐
Are you aware of any shoreline erosion problems? ☐ ☐ ☐ ☐
Are you aware of neighbours who have any erosion problems? ☐ ☐ ☐ ☐
Are there erosion control structures on the property or nearby? ☐ ☐ ☐ ☐
If YES:
  Are all approvals and licences being transferred with sale of the property? ☐ ☐ ☐ ☐

docks *See Chapter 9*
Is there a dock? ☐ ☐ ☐ ☐
If YES:
  Are there any problems with it? ☐ ☐ ☐ ☐
  Is it pulled out seasonally? ☐ ☐ ☐ ☐

water levels
Is any of the property within the 100 year floodplain? ☐ ☐ ☐ ☐
Is the basement, crawl space, or main floor at least 1.5 m (5 ft) above the floodplain? ☐ ☐ ☐ ☐
Have you ever experienced flooding or flood damage? ☐ ☐ ☐ ☐
Is the water body controlled by a dam? ☐ ☐ ☐ ☐

other
Is the beach sand all natural? ☐ ☐ ☐ ☐
Are there temperature inversions which bring smoky air down to ground level? ☐ ☐ ☐ ☐
Are there occasional odours from nearby farming or industrial operations? ☐ ☐ ☐ ☐

How Healthy is My Shoreline?

People have often asked us, "How's my shoreline doing? Is it healthy?". This simple quiz can help give you a general idea of whether your shoreline needs some help, or is at risk of having future problems. For a detailed scientific assessment, consult a local naturalist or biologist.

When assessing shoreline health, consider the area occupied by your buffer zone. *See Chapter 3*. Examine the riparian buffer – a strip at least 30 m (100 ft) wide above high water, or upland of any naturally "hard" surface such as rock or sand. Also consider your aquatic buffer – the area from high water line outward into the water.

	see page	agree	disagree	not applicable
Shoreline				
★ My shoreline is covered with native vegetation along more than 3/4 of the riparian buffer - tall grasses, wildflowers, shrubs, and trees. (Remember – turf grass is not native.)	57-58 App 2	☐	☐	☐
There are native trees and shrubs in a range of ages.	57-58, 63	☐	☐	☐
There are standing dead trees used by wildlife on or near my shoreline or bank.	63-64	☐	☐	☐
There are few, if any, invasive plants in the water or along my shoreline or bank.	61-62	☐	☐	☐
There are native aquatic plants (e.g., cattails, bulrushes) along my shoreline. (Look at nearby natural sites to see if aquatic vegetation is likely to grow in your area.)	58	☐	☐	☐
There is very little evidence of erosion such as gullies, slumping, cloudy water or loss of land.	68-69	☐	☐	☐
There are few paved areas or areas of bare ground that permit direct runoff into the water.	70	☐	☐	☐
I avoid adding fill (including sand) or yard waste along my shoreline or into the water.	66, 78	☐	☐	☐
I have a pipe, cantilever or floating dock.	80-81	☐	☐	☐
★ My shoreline or bank is free of any hard structure such as a retaining wall, paved ramp, or standard gabions (wire and rocks).	65, 75	☐	☐	☐
My shoreline attracts a wide variety of wildlife such as fish, insects, and birds.	63, 99	☐	☐	☐
Yard				
★ My sewage disposal system meets current standards, including setback from water (at least 90 m (300 ft) – more in some areas).	37-38	☐	☐	☐
I pump my septic tank every 1-3 years. (Not applicable to septic holding tanks; see glossary.)	33-34	☐	☐	☐
The edge of my lawn is more than 15 m (50 ft) from my shore or bank.	55-56	☐	☐	☐
House				
My cottage or home is 30 m (100 ft) or more from the water.	19	☐	☐	☐
I avoid using chemical fertilizers and pesticides on my lawn, yard and garden.	90-91	☐	☐	☐
I use phosphate-free soaps and detergents when cleaning, doing dishes or laundry.	87-88	☐	☐	☐

★ *factors which are essential to the health of a shoreline.*

How does my shoreline rate?

Total

Total number of statements:	17	
Less number of "not applicables" checked	– _____	
	= _____	(1)
Number of "Agrees" checked	_____	(2)
Total %: (2)_____ ÷ (1)_____ **x 100 =**	_____	(3)

ANY starred statements (★) marked "Disagree": *Your shoreline may need help.*

Over 75% AND you "Agree" with ALL of the starred statements (★): *Your shoreline is likely in good shape.*

Under 75%: *Your shoreline may need help.*

For each item you've marked "disagree", *turn to the appropriate section in this book for tips on making your shoreline a healthier place.*

To find out more about other products and programs that can help you, visit our website or fill in the Shoreline Action Checklist at the back of this book.

References

The following, in conjunction with Resources listed in each chapter, is an abridged listing of references used in the preparation of this book. A full listing is posted on our website.

A Guide to Buying and Managing Shoreland. 1998. State of Minnesota, Department of Natural Resources.

A Guide to Using Native Plants on Disturbed Land. 1996. Gerling, H.S., M.G. Willoughby, A. Schoepf, K.E. Tannas and C.A. Tannas. Alberta Agriculture, Food and Rural Development and Alberta Environmental Protection.

At Home with Wetlands: A Landowner's Guide. 1990. Joy P. Michaud. Washington State Department of Ecology Publication #90-31.

Backyard Habitat for Canada's Wildlife. 1996. Canadian Wildlife Federation. Ottawa.

Bidding the Cottage Adieu. 2001. Andrew Wagner-Chazalon. www.muskokan.com/sept_20_features.htm

Canada's Fish Habitat Law. 1991. Fisheries and Oceans Canada.

Caring for the Green Zone: Riparian Areas and Grazing Management. 1995. Barry Adams and Lorne Fitch. Cows and Fish Partnership. Lethbridge, Alberta.

Caring for Our Shores. A Handbook for Coastal Landowners in the Strait of Georgia. 1998. Bill Austin, S. Cowan, C. Wilson. Cowichan Community Land Trust Society and the Marine Ecology Station.

Caring for Shoreline Properties. Changing the way we look at owning lakefront property in Alberta. 1999. Pat Valastin. Alberta Conservation Assoc.

Clean Water – It Starts with You. Brochure series. BC Ministry of Environment, Lands and Parks.

Clean Water Guide. 1998. Manitoba Environment, Water Quality Management Section.

Cottage Water Systems. 1993 and 1999. Max Burns, Cottage Life Books. Toronto.

The Dock Primer: A Cottager's Guide to Waterfront Friendly Docks. c. 2000. Max Burns, Cottage Life and Fisheries and Oceans, Canada.

Flood Proofing Your Home. 1999. Queen's Printer for British Columbia. Victoria, BC.

Home*A*Syst: An Environmental Risk-Assessment Guide for the Home. 1997. National Home*A*Syst Program and Northeast Regional Agricultural Engineering Service, Cooperative Extension, Ithaca, New York.

Home Tips for Healthy Streams. Fisheries and Oceans Canada. (Brochure).

Horses in the Community...A Yeah or a Neigh? 1998. British Columbia Ministry of Agriculture, Fisheries and Food, Resource Management Branch.

www.lanarc.bc.ca (source of "the 4D's of Runoff Control", p. 23).

Environmental Handbook for Towed Water Sports. International Water Ski Federation. www.hoeng.com/panam/IWSFENVIRON/IWSFecPartc

Lake Care: A Property Owner's Guide to Conserving Fish Habitat in Lakes. BC Environment, Lands and Parks. (Brochure.)

Lakescaping for Wildlife and Water Quality. 2000. Carrol L. Henderson et al. Department of Natural Resources, St. Paul, Minnesota.

Life on the Edge ... Owning Waterfront Property. 1995. Michael D. Dresen and Robert Korth. UWEX-Lakes Partnership, College of Natural Resources, University of Wisconsin, Stevens Point, Wisconsin.

Living in Nature Series: The Value of Riparian Habitat and How to Care for it. South Okanagan Similkameen Stewardship Program. (Brochure).

Logging on Private Land: A Landowners Guide. 1996. South Okanagan Similkameen Stewardship Program.

NatureScape Alberta: Creating and Caring for Wildlife Habitat at Home. 2000. Myrna Pearman and Ted Pike. Red Deer River Naturalists and Federation of Alberta Naturalists, Edmonton, Alberta.

Naturescape BC. 1995. Provincial Guide. Susan Campbell and Sylvia Pincott. BC Ministry of Environment, Lands and Parks. Victoria. Also available: Guides for Southern Interior and Georgia Basin.

Oregon Small Acreages Conservation Toolbox. 1999. Washington County Soil and Water Conservation District.

Planting Shoreline Vegetation. 1994. Tree Plan Canada and Natural Resources Canada, Quebec Region, Sainte-Foy, Quebec.

Protecting BC's Aquatic Environment: A Boater's Guide. 1997. Fisheries and Oceans Canada, Coast Guard and BC Ministry of Environment, Lands and Parks.

Puget Sound Shoreline Stewardship Guidebook. 1999. Puget Sound Water Action Team, Washington. www.wa.gov/puget_sound

Riparian Rights and Public Foreshore Use in the Administration of Aquatic Crown Land. 1995. Occasional Paper No. 5. British Columbia Ministry of Environment, Lands and Parks.

Sensible Shoreland Lighting. David S. Liebl, and Robert Korth. 2000. University of Wisconsin, Extension.

Slope Stabilization and Erosion Control Using Vegetation: A Manual of Practice for Coastal Property Owners. 1993. Publication 93-30. Washington State Department of Ecology.

Soil Bioengineering for Forest Land Reclamation and Slope Stabilization. 2001. David Polster, Duncan, B.C.

Streambank Restoration Manual for B.C. 2001. David Polster. Ministry of Environment, Lands and Parks, Duncan, B.C.

The Streamkeepers Handbook: A Practical Guide to Stream and Wetland Care. 1995. Department of Fisheries and Oceans.

Streamside Revegetation Manual. Streamside Native Plants. Bowser, British Columbia. mars.ark.com/~barport/streamside.htm

"Tap Water That's Fit to Drink", by Craig Canine. 1991. *The Cottage Book: A Collection of Practical Advice.* Frank B. Edwards, Editor. Hedgehog Productions Inc.

ToxicSmart Alternatives Fact Sheet Series. Georgia Strait Alliance. Nanaimo, B.C.

Understanding Wetlands. Wetland Handbook for British Columbia's Interior. 1998. Bruno Delesalle et al. Ducks Unlimited Canada. Kamloops, BC.

Understanding, Living with, and Controlling Shoreline Erosion. A Guidebook for Shoreline Property Owners. 1997. Douglas Fuller. Tip of the Mitt Watershed Council. Conway, Michigan.

Vancouver Island Shores: Seashore Exploring for the Novice. 1998. Lynda A. Colbeck. Protected Shores Press. Lantzville, B.C. Canada.

Vegetation Management: A Guide for Puget Sound Bluff Property Owners. 1993. Publication 93-31. Washington State Department of Ecology.

Watershed Stewardship – A Guide for Agriculture. 1997. Jennifer Nener et al. Stewardship Series. Fisheries and Oceans Canada and Government of British Columbia.

Glossary

Definitions are limited to aspects which are relevant to the usage in this book, and have been simplified for ease of understanding. Note that some terms (e.g., "natural boundary", "septic system") are defined in the chapters in which they are discussed. For further detail, consult materials from the list of references.

Accretion – The deposition of water-borne sediment resulting in the addition of land to a property.

Air inversion – Occurs when a warmer air mass moves above cooler air, trapping the cooler, denser air underneath.

Algal bloom – A visible concentration of algae in or on the surface layer of a water body.

Aquaculture – The cultivation of plants or raising of animals in water.

Aquifer – A permeable subsurface zone capable of yielding quantities of groundwater to wells and springs.

Arborist – A person who is trained in the science and art of managing trees and shrubs.

Backwash – The drainwater resulting from the act of flushing out (e.g., a water softener, filter, hot tub, or swimming pool).

Bacteriologic – Having to do with bacteria.

Bed – The land upon which the water in a water body sits.

Bioengineering (Soil) – Combining living (plants) and non-living (rock, wood, brush) elements to protect eroding areas.

Breakwater – A structure (like a groin or pier) that protects a shore area or harbour from the force of waves.

Cantilever dock – A dock fixed to the shore and suspended out over the water.

Carcinogenic – A term used to describe a substance that can cause cancer.

Caveat – A formal warning; beware. *Caveat emptor*: let the buyer beware.

Concrete lattice – Cast concrete patio stone with void areas into which soil is placed for planting of ground cover.

Conservation easement – A voluntary legal agreement between a landowner and a qualified organization whereby any registered landowner is able to retain ownership of the land while transferring specific rights to its uses to an easement-holding organization, for the purpose of protecting the land's natural values on a long-term permanent basis.

Contour line – Line on a map that represents an imaginary line on the ground where the elevation above sea level is the same along its entire length.

Covenant – A written agreement between parties which outlines an obligation to do a specific action. It is typically used to restrict land use and may be registered on the land title.

Cyst – A microscopic sac which houses protozoa like *Giardia* and *Cryptosporidium* which are widespread parasites (not bacteria or viruses) that cause intestinal illnesses.

Diatomaceous earth – A fine, sharp-edged powdery substance made of diatoms (microscopic fossilized algae); used in industrial processes, and also to kill insects like ants.

Drain field – A network of pipes in which fluid (effluent) is discharged to the ground by seepage through the gravel bed into the soil or by direct evaporation into the soil.

Dredge – To widen or to clean an area with a mechanical scoop. Dredging is often done to deepen water bodies and can be damaging to aquatic ecosystems.

Effluent – The liquid waste from treated sewage or industrial processing.

Emergent – Aquatic vegetation which emerges out of the water.

Fish habitat – Spawning grounds and nursery, rearing, food supply and migration areas on which fish depend directly or indirectly in order to carry out their life processes. (Canada Fisheries Act)

Gabion – A rock-filled wire cage used for retaining walls.

Geotextile – A thick, strong, felt-like cloth used to hold soil in place beneath rock or plantings, that allows water to pass through.

Groundwater – Water that infiltrates through the ground surface and accumulates underground in porous rock or gravels.

Groundwater hydrologist – An expert in the science of water, its properties and its movement under the ground.

Gully – A channel or a valley which was created by runoff moving through the area. Water usually flows through a gully during or immediately after periods of heavy rain.

Habitat – The specific elements of the environment (aquatic, terrestrial and atmospheric) upon which a living organism depends in order to survive.

HADD – Term used by Fisheries and Oceans Canada to describe an activity which might "harmfully alter, damage or destroy fish habitat". Includes any change in fish habitat that reduces its capacity to support one or more life processes of fish.

Hantavirus – A potentially fatal respiratory disease that can be passed on to humans from mouse droppings.

Holding tank – A tank designed to hold but not treat human sewage waste. Frequent pumping is required.

Hydrofracture – A process undertaken to increase water yields of wells drilled into rock by pumping water under pressure into the well to open up new veins or flush out existing ones.

Invasive – Tending to spread or infringe. The term identifies species that can take over a given area or entire ecosystem and be detrimental to other species.

Leaching – The process by which nutrient chemicals or contaminants are dissolved and carried away by water or are moved into a lower layer of soil.

Licence of Occupation – A licence issued under the *Public Lands Act* to occupy and use Crown land for a stated purpose, e.g., a permanent water line. A Licence does not grant rights of exclusive possession.

Mercury vapour lamp – A lamp that produces light by passing an electrical current through mercury vapour.

Microclimate – The climate in the immediate surroundings; small scale.

Mooring buoy – A float that has been attached to the bottom of a water body (i.e., the bed) by a cable, line or anchor.

Native plant species – A plant species that originally occurred in an area.

Non-native species – A plant or animal that originated in another region or on another continent.

Nitrates – Chemical compounds containing nitrogen and oxygen, and an important source of the nutrient nitrogen for plants; nitrates are a major component in fertilizers.

Nutrient – A substance that nourishes. The elements nitrogen, phosphorus and potassium are important nutrients for plants.

PCBs – Polychlorinated biphenyls – A group of synthetic chemicals which accumulate in the environment and in our tissues.

Pesticides – Toxic chemicals used to eliminate or control unwanted insects, plants or other organisms. Pesticides include insecticides, herbicides and fungicides.

Phosphates – Chemical compounds containing phosphorus and oxygen; phosphorus is a nutrient necessary for the growth of plants. Phosphates are a major ingredient in many detergents and in chemical fertilizers.

Potable – Suitable for drinking.

Propagate – To grow new seedlings from seed or parent stock.

Registered society – A provincially registered non-profit group headed by a volunteer board.

Restoration – The process of returning an ecosystem to a state comparable to its original one (including structure, species composition, and functions).

Retrofit – Alteration of a building to accommodate new or changed fixtures.

Riparian – Area of land containing moist soils and moisture-loving plants that borders streams, lakes or other bodies of freshwater.

Runoff – Rainfall or snowmelt which exceeds the rate at which water can soak into the soil, resulting in flows over the land surface.

Scum – A filmy layer of impure material that floats to the top of a septic tank when the light and heavy solid materials separate.

Scupper – An opening on the side of a boat that allows water falling on deck to flow overboard.

Sediment – Particles of solid matter suspended in liquid or settling to the bottom.

Seepage – The passage of fluid through a porous medium. In the case of groundwater, seepage is groundwater that is emerging on the face of a stream bank.

Shore – The area of exposed lake bed when water levels are below the bank.

Sludge – Heavy, semi-solid, impure material that sinks to the bottom of a septic tank when the light and heavy solid materials separate.

Slumping – Collapse of earth as in a landslide.

Sodium lamp – A lamp that produces light by passing an electrical current through sodium vapour.

Soffit – The undersurface of a balcony, roof overhang or arch.

Solvent – A liquid used to dissolve another substance. Common household solvents include water and acetone.

Stair stringers – The sloping side rail of stairs which support the treads.

Submergent – Refers to aquatic vegetation which stays submerged.

Substrate – The material which forms the bed of a stream or lake.

Stewardship – A personal commitment to care for your land, sustaining or enhancing it for the enjoyment of future generations.

Swale – A shallow depression in the ground (natural or artificial) which drains runoff.

Topography – The shape of the land's surface – its physical features such as hills, valleys, cliffs and ravines.

Transpiration – The movement of water from the ground to the atmosphere via pores in plant cells.

Upland – Land that has a higher elevation than the adjacent bank, floodplain or stream terrace.

Water quality – The chemical, physical and biological characteristics of water.

Water table – The upper limit or level of water underground.

Watershed – The area of land which catches rainfall and snow, divided from the next watershed by features like ridge tops, and which drains water into a lake, stream or other water body.

Well casing – The lining which is inserted into a well as it is drilled or dug to prevent the walls from collapsing.

Acronyms

CSA – Canadian Standards Association

DFO – Fisheries and Oceans Canada

EHO – Environmental Health Officer

EPA – United States Environmental Protection Agency

EPS – Expanded Polystyrene

NSF – National Sanitation Foundation

OECD – Organization for Economic Co-operation and Development

PFD – Personal Flotation Device

SPCA – Society for the Prevention of Cruelty to Animals

SRD – Alberta Sustainable Resource Development

WIN – Water Insoluble Nitrogen

Index

Notes

Your Shoreline Action Checklist

These are the new actions I'll take and the things I'm already doing to protect my shoreline,
save time and money, and safeguard the value of my investment.

I will ✓   **see page**

shoreline

a ☐ Start a buffer strip by leaving some grass uncut near the water's edge   10, 57
b ☐ Protect a strip of native plants along my shoreline   57
c ☐ Replant native shrubs and trees along my shoreline   72
d ☐ Check regularly for invasive plants and remove them carefully   61
e ☐ Let imported beach sand erode naturally and let native plants grow back   78
f ☐ Let natural debris (e.g., rocks, fallen trees) accumulate as much as possible   66
g ☐ Build a low-impact dock (check regulations)   79
h ☐ Keep pets and/or livestock away from my shoreline or streamside   100, 121

yard

i ☐ Minimize the number of trees and shrubs cleared during construction projects   19
j ☐ Prune trees to obtain a better view, instead of removing them   59
k ☐ Reduce my use of fertilizers and pesticides   91
l ☐ Handle fuels, oil and other chemicals with great care, and be prepared for spills   29, 93
m ☐ Redirect driveway runoff into a settling/soaking area   24

house

n ☐ Use phosphate-free soaps and cleaners   88
o ☐ Use alternative cleaners like baking soda and vinegar instead of toxic products   88
p ☐ Pump my septic tank regularly (for a field system, every 1-3 years)   33
q ☐ Avoid overloading my septic system by staggering full laundry loads through the week   33
r ☐ Conserve water by using low-flow showerheads and toilets   89
s ☐ Give my visitors a Green Guest Guide (download from www.livingbywater.ca)   106

boating

t ☐ Use oil-absorbing bilge cloths, instead of bilge cleaners   112
u ☐ Practise safe refuelling   110
v ☐ Drive at no-wake speeds within 150 m (500 ft) of shore   109
w ☐ Purchase or use a 2- or 4-stroke motor that meets or betters EPA 2006 guidelines   109
x ☐ Maintain my boat motor and have it inspected regularly   109

Complete the checklist, keeping this page for your records and mail in the reply card. You'll receive a Shoreline Ambassador Certificate and will be joining with others who are helping to protect shorelines. You can also request more information about customized services:

Shoreline Home Visit:
A trained assessor visits your property and gives you suggestions on things you can do to help protect it, and prevent problems in the future. Contact your regional Living by Water office for details.

Living by Water Workshop:
Delivered to your area as a kit in a box, with presentation materials and script. You can obtain the kit from your regional Living by Water office, and arrange with a group of neighbours to hold the event. You choose how much material to cover.

www.livingbywater.ca